HUNGARIAN ART NOUVEAU

AN EXHIBITION ORGANIZED BY

THE SMITHSONIAN INSTITUTION TRAVELING EXHIBITION SERVICE

IN COOPERATION WITH

THE HUNGARIAN INSTITUTE FOR CULTURAL RELATIONS AND

THE MUSEUM OF APPLIED ARTS, BUDAPEST

1977-1979

WITH SUPPORT FROM

THE AMERICAN REVOLUTION BICENTENNIAL ADMINISTRATION

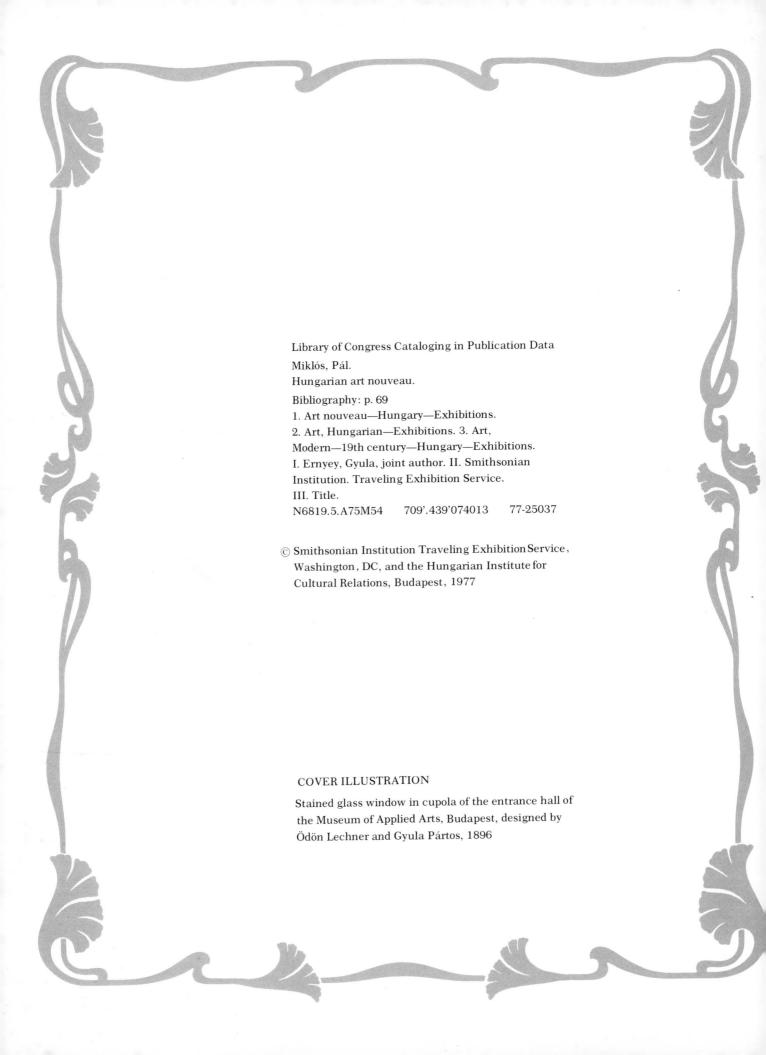

Library of Congress Cataloging in Publication Data
Miklós, Pál.
Hungarian art nouveau.
Bibliography: p. 69
1. Art nouveau—Hungary—Exhibitions.
2. Art, Hungarian—Exhibitions. 3. Art,
Modern—19th century—Hungary—Exhibitions.
I. Ernyey, Gyula, joint author. II. Smithsonian
Institution. Traveling Exhibition Service.
III. Title.
N6819.5.A75M54   709'.439'074013   77-25037

COVER ILLUSTRATION

Stained glass window in cupola of the entrance hall of
the Museum of Applied Arts, Budapest, designed by
Ödön Lechner and Gyula Pártos, 1896

FOREWORD

The exhibition presents the emergence of Art Nouveau in Hungary at the end of the 19th and beginning of the 20th centuries. Selection of the works was limited by the great distance between our two countries and by the traveling nature of the exhibition. However, we have tried to present it in a way that would reveal the circumstances of the emergence of this trend in Hungarian art, also its achievements, foreign influences and after effects.

The structure of the exhibition is as follows:

1. Introductory section to imply the aspects of the development of Hungarian art at the turn of the century; and to point out the double source of Art Nouveau, folk art and universal art.

2. The main part of the exhibition consists of concrete achievements in terms of genre and crafts with a background of a documentation of architecture and interior design.

3. Finally the exhibition closes on some examples documenting the relationship between American and Hungarian art at the turn of the century, and of the achievements of Hungarian artists working in the United States.

4. A series of slides supplements the exhibition.

The exhibition has been organized by the Hungarian Institute for Cultural Relations, Budapest, and by the Smithsonian Institution Traveling Exhibition Service. The catalogue is published by SITES. We acknowledge with thanks the help of the following institutions: the Association of the Hungarian Photo/artists, the Museum of Applied Arts, the Museum of Commerce and Catering Trade, the Hungarian National Gallery, the Museum of Ethnography, the Petőfi Literary Museum, and the National Széchenyi Library, all in Budapest, for their assistance in the selection and for the loan of works of art.

The exhibition was planned by Dr Gyula Ernyey, deputy director general of the Museum of Applied Arts, who has also compiled the catalogue, with the assistance of Ms Lilla Tompos, museologist. Ms Tompos also compiled the biographical sections.

We sincerely hope that the common endeavor of those responsible for the organization of this exhibition will result in a deeper understanding of Hungarian culture.

Dr Pál Miklós
Director
Museum of Applied Arts, Budapest

HUNGARIAN ART NOUVEAU

As the last decade of the 19th century drew to a close, art and architecture in Europe were in the grip of a dispiriting academicism: the final years of half a century of historical revival. The force that moved the French Impressionists in the 1860s was a mere ripple across the surface of the stolid products of the art academies, where rigid portraiture and sweeping historical panoramas were the norm. Architecture and the decorative arts were being stifled by the endless repetition of Renaissance and Baroque styles, and the consumer goods of a newly industrialized society that flooded the marketplace raised storms of protest from artists and craftsmen for the expediency of their fabrication; the vulgarity of their looks. The desire for change was rampant: it was felt as much a need to change society itself as to revolt against a mechanized age and the worn out decoration of the past.

In England William Morris and the arts-and-crafts movement sought a return to the beauty of the handmade object, with an emphasis on linear design culled from sources such as Celtic illuminated manuscripts, and Persian, Moorish and Turkish decorative ornament. Others, who recognized that the heavy tread of progress could not be halted, strove to put the new technological advances to artistic use in the idealistic hope that elegant, well-designed objects might be mass-produced and made available to everyone.

At the end of the century it was the monumental figure of Paul Gauguin who carried the standard for the artist's rebellion against the mores of a bourgeois society grown stale: a capitalist society,

epitomized in part by the advent of the department store stocked with cheap goods in imitation-historic patterns.

Artists, architects and craftsmen were searching for an original expression—something to match the new age: a basic purity, the essence in things, the beauty of functionalism. Since history repeats itself, so we are told, it comes as no surprise that the outcome of all this striving, namely the movement called Art Nouveau, should have its roots firmly buried in the past. The revelation of recently imported Japanese prints, the renewed interest in medieval, primitive and folk art forms produced a style that was to catapult across Europe, rapidly reached the shores of America, and left no country untouched by its influence.

In literature it was the heirs of Charles Baudelaire, Symbolist writers and poets like Stéphane Mallarmé, Paul Verlaine, J.-K. Huysmans, Maurice Maeterlinck and Hugo von Hofmannsthal who delved beneath the brittle surface of life to reveal the seamier side of men's thoughts. It was perhaps no coincidence that Sigmund Freud in Vienna was publishing his discoveries in psychoanalysis at this time. Gauguin had said, "art is an abstraction; derive this abstraction from Nature while dreaming before it"; and thus the Symbolist painters desired to establish their own world of forms inspired by Nature and the dream, and thereby challenging the classicists rule of reason.

Architects were more pragmatic. The use of iron and glass as building materials provided them at last with the opportunity to break through to dynamic new spatial concepts. Two structures that pointed the way were Scottish architect Charles Rennie MacKintosh's sombre, geometric Glasgow School of Art (1898–99), and Gustave Eiffel's tower in Paris (1889), the latter strongly influencing the work of one of the greatest Art Nouveau architects, Victor Horta in Belgium. In Spain Antonio Gaudi worked in a highly idiosyncratic manner, his buildings seeming to "grow" out of the ground in flowing, organic curves, and his decorative ironwork twisting fantastically in every direction. With, among others, the Paris Metro stations of Hector Guimard, the pioneering work of Otto Wagner in Vienna—who used prefabricated concrete, marble cladding, ceramic tiles, copper and aluminum in his striking new buildings—the face of Europe was being slowly altered.

But it was in the decorative and applied arts that the main impact of Art Nouveau was felt. Interior designers, furniture makers, silversmiths, jewelers, glass and porcelain manufacturers all embraced the new style; the trailing, twisting stem-like forms and stylized flower patterns appearing everywhere.

In Hungary, where for centuries the fronts of houses have been carved and decorated, clothing heavily embroidered, articles of everyday use in the home covered with designs, Art Nouveau fell upon fertile ground. Here, as elsewhere, artists were intent on breaking away from the graying pall of industrial development and the bonds of upper middle class taste. Hungary was still the restless monarchy of Francis Joseph I of Austria, but had governed itself since 1867. Nationalist feelings ran high. Politically backward, power was still in the hands of the landowners, the mass of the people having little or no say in their situation or in their future. Artists were obliged to look for support from the well-off bourgeoisie, and in their efforts to win through to a nobler, more spiritual and poetic life, restricted their revolt purely to the realm of art.

The International Exhibition of Paris in 1900 was a triumph for Art Nouveau, and Hungarian artists won many prizes for their work. The then director of the Museum of Applied Arts in Budapest, Jenő Radisics, selected about one hundred pieces from this exhibition, ranging from furniture to jewels, from pottery to bronze plaques, from glass to cutlery. Yet Art Nouveau did not truly blossom in Hungary until the first decades of the 20th century, thus justifying its being referred to by the German name, *Jugendstil*, "young style."

Although some influence stemmed from nearby Vienna, Hungarian artists received inspiration from all parts of Europe. A large number of Hungarians studied in Munich, for example, but the attraction of Paris soon proved to be the most enduring. Similarly Italians and Swedes, English and Austrians came to Hungary for long or short periods to fulfill commissions or as guests of artists' colonies or rich art patrons. Some of these were world-famous, such as the Englishman Walter Crane, architect-engineers like Gustave Eiffel, or some who acquired fame in Hungary only, like Leo Belmonte, who was in fact Swedish.

The last decades of the 19th century saw the Hungarian manufacturing industry gaining ground, and the building of the public transportation network. Budapest, along with several other major towns, underwent rapid expansion at this time, and there was a growing affluence in these urban centers. Public building was largely in the area of cultural institutions: museums, theatres, schools, even the famous zoo in the capital, and some fine examples of Art Nouveau architecture remain.

Ödön Lechner was an architect who consciously tried to create a Hungarian form of expression, and his first major commission was a new building for the Museum of Applied Arts, completed in 1896, the year when Hungary celebrated its 1,000th anniversary. The building is permeated with the then fashionable idea of the Oriental origin of the Hungarian peoples: the handling of space, surface ornamentation and window shapes are reminiscent of Muslim India. In his most successful work, the Postal Savings Bank, Lechner borrowed from Hungarian peasant art—the so-called "Hungarian popular style"—his surface decoration. Thus Lechner's *oeuvre* represents two characteristic trends of Hungarian Art Nouveau: one, an inspiration based on an Oriental heritage; the other, a transformation of the richly decorative motifs of Hungarian folk art.

The interest in things Oriental inspired the early work of the Symbolist poet Endre Ady, who later found support for his revolutionary ideas in the Hungarian working class movement. A similar revelation was granted to the painter, Tivadar Csontváry, whose wanderings in the East helped produce his grandiose visions. But other artists were attracted as well, such as Pál Horti and István Medgyaszay. The existence of the Museum of Eastern Asiatic Arts in Hungary, founded by Ferenc Hopp, is proof of the spell cast by the Orient at this time.

The rediscovery of folk art was naturally related to the idea of creating a national style, and, besides the new subjects that were offered, heroes of the old Hungarian legends were revived. One of the characteristic ornamental elements of Hungarian folk art is a sequence or composition of stylized flowers, used particularly in textiles, garments, homespuns, embroidery, embroidered felt and in wood carving. An appreciation of folk music began during this period from which the work of Bartók and Kodály was to blossom. The result of these interests fostered a new development in the folk arts of some regions: the more modest ornamentation around Mezőkövesd was replaced by a curious, rich, and almost tawdry colored flower pattern; the lace produced at Halas was designed and encouraged by an artist and teacher, Árpád Dékáni. Popular folk motifs were to be found on book covers, leather folders, and household fabrics, remolded by the meandering line of Art Nouveau.

At the turn of the century a group of artists settled at Gödöllő and established their own carpet-weaving workshop. As followers of the English Pre-Raphaelites and William Morris, they wove figurative compositions: themes from the Hungarian heroic legends, and figures and anecdotes from Hungarian history. Members of the Gödöllő group also designed murals and large stained-glass windows; the most notable example of their work is at the Palace of Culture in Marosvásárhely (today Tirgu-Mures) built in 1907 by the architects Marcell Komor and Dezső Jakab.

Among the most original products of Hungarian Art Nouveau are the ceramics created by Vilmos Zsolnay. Zsolnay's technical inventions at his factory in Pécs resulted in a variegated faience, with glazes of the most marvelous colors. His unique designs, drawing from the linear tradition of European Art Nouveau and remodeled with elements from the Hungarian style, brought him international fame.

There was only one individual who practiced in all branches of the arts, and that was the painter József Rippl-Rónai. He lived and studied in Paris until 1900, and knew the eminent French figures of the period. He experimented with painting on glass, designed carpets, ceramics and glass, and tried his hand at furniture designing. From a complete set of furniture designed by him for Count Andrássy, only a wall-hanging in silk embroidery survives. Called "The Woman in the Red Dress," it is a popular and often reproduced piece: something like the symbol of Hungarian Art Nouveau.

The eminent art critic of the time, Károly Lyka, wrote in 1902, "whatever is generally called the style of Art Nouveau is identical in its origin, essence and effect, with whatever is normally considered to be the Hungarian style. . . ." And, "Hungarian art has never been in a more advantageous position than today for formulating the first accents of a Hungarian style. . . ."

Art Nouveau in Hungary was not the

movement it was in Western Europe. There was no periodical, no organized group or exhibitions, and even the single workshop, at Gödöllő, was a latecomer. It was, rather, a European and Central East European artistic trend which had its supporters and followers, theoreticians as well as artists: a complex structure of intellectual and artistic effort complementing Hungarian cultural life around the turn of the century. There coexisted the Hungarian "Impressionists" of the school of Nagybánya, the naturalism of the genre painters, and the entire canon of "plastic" classicism; the eclectic "palace-style" buildings, and the strict solemnity of memorial statues, as well as the presence of the Symbolist painters and poets. The colorful artistic life, the age-old problems raised by questions of fine art and the applied arts made this period an exhilarating one. The Hungarian Museum of Applied Arts, an independent institution, was founded in 1872, and after two and a half decades it moved into its own new building, to house for all to study examples of the art "industry" and relics of past ages.

Talented people in the applied arts were, besides the painter József Rippl-Rónai, Pál Horti who designed furniture, ceramics and textiles; Ede Thoroczkai Wigand, an architect and furniture designer; Oszkár Tarján, who rejuvenated jewelry design, and István Sovánka, a master glassmaker. The sculptor, Ö. Fülöp Beck, worked in decorative metal and made coins; another painter, János Vaszary, designed fabric and wall-carpets.

Improved printing techniques gave rise to the poster, which in Hungary, as in other parts of Europe, were frequently designed by outstanding painters. Rippl-Rónai, Vaszary, and Károly all did posters, but by the early years of 1900 the first generation of graphic artists specializing in poster design appeared; the best of these were: Géza Faragó and Mihály Biró. Book illustration and design, small graphics, prints and postage stamps also proved popular. However, it was not long before the sheer volume of printed matter being circulated caused an inevitable decline in standard and the linear quality of Art Nouveau was reduced to a fashionable mannerism.

The Hungarian Art Nouveau style in architecture is represented by Géza Maróti, who created his main body of work abroad, namely the Hungarian pavilion at the Venice Biennale of 1909, and buildings in Mexico and in the United States. Two stayed in Europe: Károly Kós did a few buildings in Budapest and a church in Zebegény, but his major contributions are in Transylvania; István Medgyaszay designed the Hungarian pavilion for the International Exhibition in Milan in 1906, built the theatre at Veszprém in 1908, and the studios and a workshop for the artists at Gödöllő. Around 1932 he undertook major architectural commissions in Bombay.

The strange world of tales by Anna Lesznai became well-known abroad, and her embroidered cushions and illustrations for children's books carried the motifs of Hungarian folk art to America.

It is a curious fact that there has never been an exhibition in Hungary of Hungarian Art Nouveau, even though Hungarian artists participated in the series of international exhibitions at the beginning of the century, carrying off many prizes and receiving high praise. It has taken the present generation to rediscover Art Nouveau and to appreciate why the style was so valuable to our age. Besides defeating the prevailing mode of historic revivalism at the end of the 19th century, it is generally agreed upon by scholars and art historians that Art Nouveau was the first true synthesis of the plastic arts. It permeated every area of artistic activity and allowed its practitioners to experiment in ways not possible before. The discoveries and achievements made then, still affect us now.

Dr Pál Miklós, Director
Museum of Applied Arts, Budapest

HUNGARIAN-AMERICAN CONTACTS AT THE TURN OF THE CENTURY

This is the first time such a large-scale exhibtion of Hungarian Art Nouveau has been presented to an American audience. The work of some individuals may however be familiar, since as early as the turn of the century considerable contact was established between American and Hungarian designers.

News of what was happening in America was spread by the Hungarian press, and particularly by a magazine on the decorative and applied arts called *Magyar Iparművészet,* which covered the spectrum of international activity: including leading articles on the World Fairs. It followed therefore that American-made artifacts appeared quite early in Hungary. In 1890 the Museum of Applied Arts acquired Rookwood ceramics, and in 1898 mounted an exhibition of Tiffany glass, together with a display of American posters designed by Louis J. Rhead, Ethel Reed, Maxfield Parrish and Edward Penfield. The Museum eventually acquired some examples of Tiffany glass, and his methods influenced many Hungarian glassmakers. A critic, József Diner-Dénes, commented at the time that America was, "imbued with an artistic spirit and [has] an imposing industry both in extent and depth."

The presence of American graphics, book illustrations and ceramics had no small effect in Hungary, although it must be said that, because of geographic location, Hungarian arts and the country's intellectual life were more deeply influenced by what was emanating from nearer West European countries, and to a lesser extent, France and England at the time.

The St Louis World's Fair in 1904 saw the first appearance of Hungarian arts and crafts in the New World. The Hungarian government commissioned architects Zoltán Bálint and Lajos Jámbor, the designers Ödön Faragó, Pál Horti, Géza Maróti and Ede Thoroczkai Wigand to design the installation. Sixteen designers and 48 craftsmen participated; they included Aladár Kőrösfői-Kriesch, Sándor Nagy, Oszkár Tarján, Miksa Róth, István Sovánka and Miklós Zsolnay. The Hungarian applied arts section was allotted a 600 square-meter space in the Manufacturers Building, where Pál Horti designed a typical Hungarian memorial building with four turrets and a courtyard. The exhibition, presenting works mainly in the spirit of Art Nouveau, was a great success: besides the laurels received—the grand prix, gold, silver and bronze medals—some Hungarians received commissions from the Americans. Pál Horti remained in the United States until 1906, designing for a number of American firms.

The St Louis experience was a revelation to the visiting Hungarians, as well as to other foreign participants. As impressive as the American achievement was to all, some visitors questioned the outcome of a meeting between American artists and American industry on so large a scale. The mass production of items having great functional and social significance but produced without the aid of artistic talent, such as the Gillette safety razor, the small Kodak camera and the Model-T Ford, seemed an inevitable result.

However, many Hungarians contributed to this progress. Of all who worked in America at this period the artist-architect Béla Takách is perhaps the best remembered. He was a designer at the Stein & Roth Company, did the interiors for the Fleischmann residence and the ten-story Hotel Balladaire. From 1902 onward he worked in the studios of Louis Comfort Tiffany.

Géza Maróti was commissioned by the architect of the Palacio de Bellas Artes in Mexico to design the interiors and ornamentation of the building. Maróti in turn invited his Hungarian colleagues over to participate: the glass ceiling was designed by Aladár Kőrösfői-Kriesch and executed by Miksa Róth. The extraordinary glass stage curtain, representing a colorful landscape in glittering hues, was designed by Maróti and made by the Tiffany firm. Maróti moved to the United States in the 1920s, and went on to become one of the early pioneers of Art Moderne, or Art Deco as it is now known. He was invited by his old friend the Finnish architect, Eliel Saarinen, to execute some building ornamentation at Cranbrook Academy of Art, Bloomfield Hills, Michigan (the president of the Cranbrook fine arts department from 1932 was the Hungarian painter Zoltán Sepeshy, who arrived in the States at the end of the First World War). Maróti worked out of Detroit during this period, 1926-32. He did the ornamentation for Albert Kahn's huge Fisher building in Detroit and the ceiling murals for the Hudson Motor Company. With Kahn, he worked on the Times building and the Livingstone monument, as well as executing the mosaic designs for Chicago Radio City.

Among the numbers of Hungarians who fled to the United States in the '20s and '30s to escape the disastrous events threatening in Europe was the architect József Bábolnay, who had worked with Lechner, the prominent practitioner of Art Nouveau architecture in Hungary. Bábolnay landed in New York in 1924, where—between 1930 and 1931—he built the first television theatre. The sculptor Dezső Lányi and writer/printer Anna Lesznai lived in the United States from the 1930s. The two most famous of these *émigrés* were László Moholy-Nagy and Marcel Breuer, both of whom arrived in 1937. Their work signified a new period in European and American culture, but this must be the subject of another exhibition.

The Hungarians who went to America in the early years of the century paved the way for their successors and helped perpetuate the spirit of cooperation and cultural exchange between the two countries. For this they are duly remembered.

Dr Gyula Ernyey
Deputy Director General
Museum of Applied Arts, Budapest

4

67

165

184

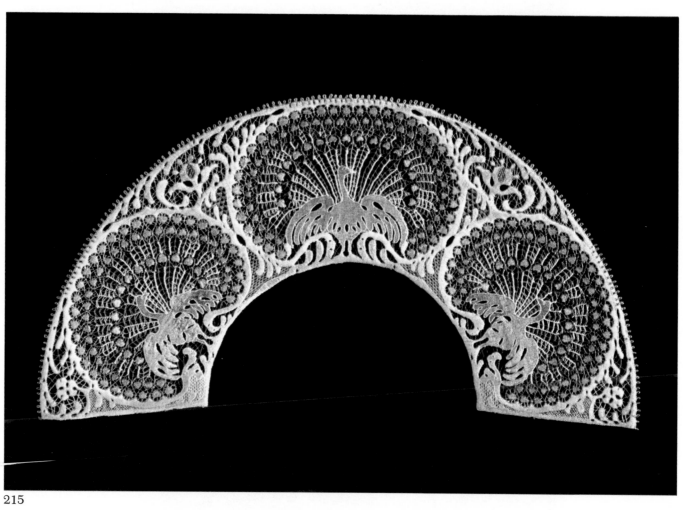

215

220

CATALOGUE

Dimensions are given in centimeters; height precedes width and depth.

*An asterisk denotes works that are not in the exhibition
but are represented by a photograph.

**A double asterisk denotes works that are illustrated in the catalogue.

FOLK ART

1
Embroidered bedsheet border,
Mezőkövesd, 19th century
Flaxen linen, embroidered with
colored silk thread,
21 x 144 cm
Museum of Applied Arts, Budapest

2
Apron, Mezőkövesd, 19th century
Black satin, embroidered with
colored silk thread,
65 x 101 cm
Museum of Applied Arts, Budapest

3
Woman's waistcoat, *kuzsu*,
Mezőkövesd, ca. 1900
Whitened sheepskin, red and black
leather appliqué, colored silk
embroidery, fringes mounted with
copper rings; length of back: 41 cm;
sleeve length: 59 cm
Museum of Ethnography, Budapest

4**
Embroidered portion of Hungarian
shepherd's cloak, *aszaj*,
Hajdúböszömény, late 19th century
White felt cloth, embroidered with
wool thread,
47 x 30 cm
Museum of Ethnography, Budapest

5
Jug, *bokály*, Transylvania, 19th
century
Lead-glazed pottery,
24.2 cm high
Museum of Applied Arts, Budapest

6
Jug, *bokály*, Transylvania, late 19th
century
Lead-glazed pottery,
21.7 cm high
Museum of Applied Arts, Budapest

7
Jug, *bokály*, Transylvania, late 19th
century
Lead-glazed pottery,
22.5 cm high
Museum of Applied Arts, Budapest

8
Pillowfront, Kalotaszeg, 19th century
Flaxen linen, embroidered with
brown wool thread,
52 x 61 cm
Museum of Applied Arts, Budapest

9
Pillowfront, Kalotaszeg, 19th century
Flaxen linen, embroidered with
black wool thread,
50 x 67 cm
Museum of Applied Arts, Budapest

10
Hornkerchief, Kalotaszeg, 19th
century
Flaxen linen, embroidered with red
wool thread,
22 x 158 cm
Museum of Applied Arts, Budapest

11**
Pillow, Kalotaszeg, 19th century
Flaxen linen, embroidered with blue
wool thread,
46 x 60 cm
Museum of Applied Arts, Budapest

4

11

ARCHITECTURE, INTERIOR DECORATION

12

FARAGÓ, Ödön (1869–1935)

An artist-craftsman, Faragó studied in Vienna and became a draftsman in a Viennese furniture manufacturing firm. In 1890–1891 he participated in the interior decoration of the House of Parliament of Budapest. He also helped design the Hungarian pavilions at the international exhibitions in Paris in 1900, Turin in 1902, Milan in 1906, and Philadelphia in 1927. He designed the interiors of several public buildings in Budapest.

12**
Sideboard, 1897
Carved oak with copper decoration,
193 x 124 x 41 cm
Made by János Turnherr
Museum of Applied Arts, Budapest

13**
Chair, 1898
Carved oak with leather seat,
decorated with copper nails,
100 x 59 x 42 cm
Made by József Nagy
Museum of Applied Arts, Budapest

GYÖRGYI, Dénes (1886–1961)

Architect, designer, professor at the School of Applied Arts Györgyi, at the beginning of his career, worked in a recognizably Hungarian style. Later, certain eclectic features appeared, and, from the end of the 1920s, his work was characterized by an understanding of the International Style in modern architecture. Some of his outstanding achievements are: a school

13

in Budapest (with Károly Kós) 1911–12; the Déri Museum in Debrecen (with Aladár Münnich) 1923–29; the Hungarian pavilions at the international exhibitions in Barcelona in 1929 (with Miklós Menyhért); in Brussels in 1935, and in Paris in 1937.

14
School on the Városmajor Street, Budapest, 1910–12 (with Károly Kós)

HEGEDŰS, Ármin (1969–1945)

An architect, Hegedűs, in partnership with Henrik Bőhm, built a number of hotels, hospitals, resorts and other public buildings. One of their most characteristic works is the Török's Bank in Budapest. Together with Artúr Sebestyén and Izidor Sterk Hegedűs won the design competition for the Gellért Hotel and Spa.

15**
The Török's Bank, Budapest, 1906 (with Henrik Bőhm)

16
Gellért Hotel and Spa, Budapest, 1911–1918 (with Artúr Sebestyén and Izidor Sterk)

HORTI, Pál (1865–1907)

A painter and designer, Horti was a prominent practitioner of Hungarian Art Nouveau. He obtained his degree at the School of Decorative Arts, Budapest, then studied painting in Munich, Paris and London. From 1890 he taught at the municipal Industrial Drawing School. He founded an independent graphics reproduction firm in Budapest, and his activities soon broadened to include most areas of the arts. He participated in the international exhibitions of Paris, Turin and St Louis. His success at the St Louis World's Fair brought him a number of commissions in America. He toured Mexico, and attempted to return home via the Far East, but he died upon reaching Bombay. His work was free of the excesses of Art Nouveau and at their best is characterized by an individual interpretation of the Belgian and English trends.

17**
Sideboard, 1900
Oak and ebony, with brass locks and ornament,
186 x 135 x 42 cm
Made by Pál Tálos
Museum of Applied Arts, Budapest

18**
Armchair, 1902
Carved oak, upholstered in velvet-plush,
110 x 57.5 x 48 cm
Made by Imre Mahunka
Museum of Applied Arts, Budapest

19*
The Hungarian section of the St. Louis World's Fair, 1904
From original photographs illustrated in *Magyar Iparmüvészet*, (Hungarian Applied Arts review, 1904)

20
Furniture designs for American factories, 1904–1905
From original photographs illustrated in *Magyar Iparmüvészet*, (Hungarian Applied Arts review, 1907

KÓS, Károly (1883-1977)

Architect, painter, graphic artist and writer, Károly Kós received his degree at the Budapest Technical University. At first he worked in the studio of Móric Pogány and later that of Géza Maróti. He studied the folk art of his homeland and Transylvania, which inspired the ornamentation on his buildings and in his graphic work. He participated in the design of several public buildings, such as: the pavilions at the Budapest Zoo (with Dezső Zrumeczky) 1909–1910; a church at Zebegény (with Béla Jánszky) 1908–1909; the school on Városmajor St., Budapest (with Dénes Györgyi) 1910–1911; a church at Kolozsvár, Cluj, 1912–1913; the Székely Museum and the Reformed Girls' Grammer School at Sepsiszentgyörgy, 1911–1912, and the Exhibition Hall, Kolozsvár, 1943. He has published plays, novels, and books on Hungarian folk art and popular architecture, and illustrated many others.

21**
Church, Zebegény, 1908–1909 (with Béla Jánszky)

22
Houses for workers and civil servants, Kispest, Budapest, 1912–1913

KOZMA, Lajos (1884–1948)

An architect, designer and graphic artist, Kozma graduated at the Technical University of Budapest. Between 1910 and 1913 he worked in the office of architect Béla Lajta. In 1913 he founded the Budapest Workshop, after the example of the Wiener Werkstätte in Austria. Later he was appointed to the Department of Interior Design at the Technical University and, in 1925, was decorated with a gold medal. He became director of the College of Applied Arts in 1946. His work was the linking point between Hungarian Art Nouveau and the ideas of a younger generation influenced by the Bauhaus.

23**
Interior of Rózsavölgyi's Music and

15

17

18

Bookshop, Budapest, 1911–1912
(with Béla Lajta)

LAJTA, Béla (1873–1920)

An architect who graduated at the Technical University of Budapest, Béla Lajta toured Italy, Germany and England, and then worked with Norman Shaw in London. His first projects were done partly in collaboration with Ödön Lechner: the Schmiedl family vault, the Szirma residence, a fire station in Zenta, the Kossuth Mausoleum. The last period of his activity is characterized by the school on Vas Street and the Rózsavölgyi's House in Budapest. This period was a revolutionary one in the history of modern Hungarian architecture, and Lajta was its first outstanding figure.

24
Almshouse, Budapest, 1908–1911

25**
School, Vas Street, Budapest,
1910–1913

26**
Rózsavölgyi's Music and Bookshop,
1911–1912

LECHNER, Ödön (1845–1914)

An architect, Lechner studied in Budapest and later at the Academy of Architecture in Berlin. He designed several apartment houses with Gyula Pártos. In 1874 he went to Paris where he worked with architect C. Parent. Returning home he worked again with Pártos and they completed several public buildings together. Lechner endeavored to create a Hungarian national style by using the ornamental motifs of Hungarian folk art, incorporated with traditions from Indian architecture. His work had a strong influence on his contemporaries. Some of his outstanding buildings are: the Town Hall, Kecskemét, 1892–1894; in Budapest, the Museum of Applied Arts, 1894–1896, the Geological Institute, 1898–1899, and the Postal Savings Bank, 1899–1901. He also published books and articles on architecture.

27**
Museum of Applied Arts, Budapest,
1894–1896 (with Gyula Pártos)

28**
Geological Institute, Budapest,
1898–1899

29**
Postal Savings Bank, Budapest,
1899–1902

MARÓTI, Géza (1878–1941)

Sculptor, architect and applied artist Maróti studied in Budapest and Vienna. In his early years he worked as an ornamental sculptor. He made his international reputation with his design for the applied arts section at the 1906 International Fair in Milan. He designed the interior and exterior decoration of the Mexican National Theatre in 1912. He worked in the United States between 1926 and 1932, making the bronzes, mosaics and murals for the Fisher Building in Detroit and the marble and bronze figures at the lighthouse of the Livingstone Memorial on Belle Isle.

30*
Entrance of the Hungarian Pavilion,
Venice Exhibition, 1908
(Reconstructed in 1959)
Photograph 30 x 36 cm; original
negative 9 x 12 cm
Museum of Applied Arts, Budapest

31**
The "Duck Salon" at the Milan
exhibition, 1906
Original photograph, 29.2 x 39.5 cm
Present photograph 27 x 36 cm
Museum of Applied Arts, Budapest

32*
Glass curtain for the National
Theatre, Mexico City, 1912
Made by the Louis C. Tiffany
Company, New York
Negative 9 x 12 cm
Present photograph 60 x 80 cm

33
Design for Glass House, 1932
Pencil on paper,
24.5 x 16.6 cm
Museum of Applied Arts, Budapest

34
Design for Glass House, 1932
Pencil on paper,
23 x 16.4 cm
Museum of Applied Arts, Budapest

35*
Details of the Fisher Building,
Detroit, 1928–1930
Negative: (a) 6 x 6 cm (b) 9 x 14 cm
(c) 9 x 14 cm
Museum of Applied Arts, Budapest
Present photograph 60 x 80 cm

36
Mosaic design for the main entrance
of the Radio City Building, New
York, 1932
Colored pencil on paper,
18.7 x 15.5 cm
Museum of Applied Arts, Budapest

37
Radio City. Design for glass relief:
center part, 1932
Pencil on paper,
16.4 x 10.2 cm
Museum of Applied Arts, Budapest

38
Design for the Hudson Motor

23

23

Company, 1932
Pencil on paper,
18.8 x 7 cm
Museum of Applied Arts, Budapest

39
Design for mosaics, Radio City
Building, Detroit, 1932
Original photograph: (a) 11.5 x 23.5
cm (b) 11.5 x 23.5 cm
Present photograph: (a) 18 x 37 cm
(b) 18 x 37 cm
Museum of Applied Arts, Budapest

MEDGYASZAY, István (1877–1959)

As an architect and writer, Medgyaszay was a prominent representative of
the Hungarian style in the early 20th
century. In 1906 he won a gold medal
for his design for the Hungarian pavilion at the international exhibition in
Milan. In 1908 he built a theatre at
Veszprém in reinforced concrete, and
in 1909 rebuilt the theatre at Sopron.
He won first prize for his design for a
National Theatre in 1913. He built
apartment houses, public buildings
and churches. In India in 1932 he designed a theatre and a number of
palaces for the Indian princes.

40
Theatre, Veszprém, 1908

THOROCZKAI WIGAND, Ede (1870–1945)

An architect and designer, Thoroczkai
Wigand studied in Budapest, Munich
and Paris. He built several small
houses in Budapest and its vicinity,
also in Transdanubia and Transylvania. Under the guidance of Imre
Steindl he participated in designing
the roof of the House of Parliament
and the hall of graphics at the
Museum of Fine Arts. The furniture
he designed at the turn of the century
was usually structured from large,
continuous sheets. The folk art of
Marosvásárhely and Kalotaszeg in
Transylvania had an impact on his
furniture designs. Between 1922 and
1934 he taught at the School of
Applied Arts. He was also active in the
field of literature and did his own book
illustrations.

41*
Sideboard, 1902
Palisander, rosewood, cedar, with
silver-plated locks and ornament,
169 x 168 x 60 cm
Made by József Mocsai
Museum of Applied Arts, Budapest

42*
Design for girls room, ca. 1900
Negative: 24 x 31 cm
Present photograph 60 x 80 cm
Museum of Applied Arts, Budapest

26

24

25

25

25

25

27

27

27

26

28

29

31

GRAPHICS

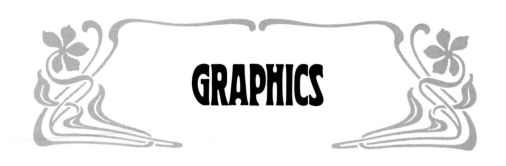

43

47

50

DIVÉKY, József (1887–1951)

A graphic artist, Divéky studied at the Academy of Vienna and the School of Applied Arts. He lived in Switzerland between 1918 and 1941, and after 1945 moved to Sopron, West Hungary. He was chiefly a book illustrator and the main body of his work is in the collection of the Liszt Ferenc Museum of Sopron, where a commemorative exhibition was organized in 1952.

43**
The Bridge, before 1914
Etching,
35 x 24 cm
Hungarian National Gallery,
Budapest

44
The Pilgrim, before 1914
Etching,
36 x 24 cm
Hungarian National Gallery,
Budapest

45
The Island of Happiness, 1917
Etching,
29 x 27 cm
Hungarian National Gallery,
Budapest

HONTI, Nándor (1878–1935)

A painter and graphic artist, Honti began his studies in Munich and Nagybánya under the guidance of Simon Hollósy; he later attended the Académie Julian in Paris. Between 1903 and 1906, he lived in the United States, then returned to Budapest and worked for the newspaper *Ujság* as an illustrator. After the First World War he emigrated to the States.

46a
Young Couple, 1903
Lithograph,
25.7 x 16.7 cm

46b
Célèbre valse lente hongroise, 1903
Lithograph,
17.5 x 15 cm

46c
Harvesters, 1903
Lithograph,
13.5 x 16.7 cm

46d
Returning Harvesters, 1903
Lithograph,
19.8 x 17.7 cm
Hungarian National Gallery,
Budapest

KÖVESHÁZI KALMÁR, Elza (1876–1956)

A sculptor, Kövesházi Kalmár studied in Munich and subsequently worked in Vienna, Paris and Florence. She returned to Budapest after the First World War, making chiefly small plastic ornaments and monuments to the deceased. The impact of Viennese Art Nouveau may be traced in her drawings.

47**
Detail of a forest, ca. 1901
Chromolithograph,
22 x 19.5 cm
Hungarian National Gallery,
Budapest

48
Thawing, ca. 1901
Chromolithograph
14.5 x 21.5 cm
Hungarian National Gallery,
Budapest

49
Twilight, 1901
Chromolithograph,
16.5 x 19.5 cm
Hungarian National Gallery,
Budapest

NAGY, Sándor (1868–1950)

A painter and graphic artist, Sándor Nagy studied in Budapest, Rome and Paris. Returning to Hungary he settled down at Gödöllő where he participated in the establishment of the artists' colony. He painted frescoes, landscapes, symbolic compositions; made etchings, designs for glass windows, and Gobelin cartoons. He also designed leather and woodwork. He taught carpet weaving at Gödöllő, and with his wife Laura Kriesch illustrated several books.

50**
Woman in the Garden, 1908
Etching,
22 x 13.5 cm
Hungarian National Gallery,
Budapest

RIPPL-RÓNAI, József (1861–1927)

Painter, graphic artist and designer, Rippl-Rónai studied in Vienna and Munich and went to Paris in 1887, where he worked in the studio of Mihály Munkácsy. He met and made friends with the Nabis: Edouard Vuillard, Pierre Bonnard, Maurice Denis and Aristide Maillol. In 1892 he moved to Neuilly where he was to remain for ten years. At the end of the 1890s he designed objects in the spirit of Art Nouveau. In 1902 he left France and settled down in Kaposvár. He tried to unite the principles of Impressionism and Post-Impressionism in his works, and after 1910, pointillist, Post-Impressionist and Art Nouveau elements are combined in his painting. After the First World War he returned again to a free-spirited

Impressionism. He is one of the best known Hungarian painters, with work in the collections of the Hungarian National Gallery, the Museum of Applied Arts and the Museum of Kaposvár (which is named after him).

51**
Sitting Woman in the Garden, 1896
Chromolithograph,
22 x 17 cm
Hungarian National Gallery,
Budapest

52
Invitation card for the Journalists'
Association Ball, 1899
Chromolithograph,
17 x 42 cm
Hungarian National Gallery,
Budapest

Invitation card for the Journalists'
Association Ball, 1899
Chromolithograph,
17 x 42 cm
Hungarian National Gallery,
Budapest

53
Illustration for *Les Vierges*, ca. 1900
Lithograph,
22 x 17 cm
Hungarian National Gallery,
Budapest

54**
Illustration for *Les Vierges*, 1896
Chromolithograph,
22 x 17 cm
Hungarian National Gallery,
Budapest

TICHY, Gyula (1879–1920)

A painter and graphic artist, Tichy was the pupil of Bertelan Székely at the Academy of Fine Arts in Budapest, and later studied under Simon Hollósy in Nagybánya. His work reflected the spirit of the Nagybánya School.

55**
Caprice and Will, 1908
Woodcut,
20 x 18.3 cm
Hungarian National Gallery,
Budapest

56
Moment and Millenary, 1910
Linocut,
22 x 12.5 cm
Hungarian National Gallery,
Budapest

VASZARY, János (1867–1939)

A painter and teacher, Vaszary studied in Budapest, in Munich and at the Académie Julian in Paris. He began as a Post-Impressionist, and was then a disciple of Puvis de Chavannes. Later he returned to

51

54

plein-air Naturalism and finally developed a fresh form close to Expressionism. His work was witty and decorative and he greatly influenced the Hungarian avant-garde. He won several prizes at home and abroad and his work can be found in the collections of foreign as well as Hungarian museums. The Hungarian National Gallery mounted a commemorative exhibition in 1961.

57**
Waiting for the Omnibus, 1903
Chromolithograph,
33 x 48 cm
Hungarian National Gallery,
Budapest

58
Spring, 1912
Chromolithograph,
32.5 x 42 cm
Hungarian National Gallery,
Budapest

55

57

PHOTOS

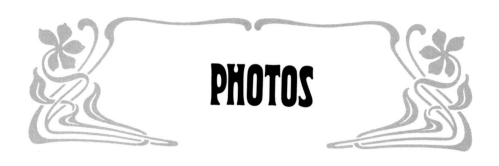

60

SZÉKELY, Aladár (1870–1940)

Székely was a photographer. He studied in Gyula and opened a studio in Orosháza. Later he went to Germany to study and work then returned to Budapest where he opened a studio in 1906. He belonged to the intellectual circle around the literary review *Nyugat* and was a friend of the writers. He made his most outstanding portraits of them, particularly of Endre Ady. In his honour the city of Gyula founded an art prize in 1966.

59
Interior, 1890–1908
Photograph 22 x 22.5 cm;
negative, 8 x 8 cm
The Association of Hungarian
Photographers, Budapest

60**
The Artist's wife at the seashore,
1890–1908
Photograph 14 x 29.5 cm;
negative, 9 x 18 cm
The Association of Hungarian
Photographers, Budapest

61
Picnic in May, 1890–1908
Photograph 22 x 29 cm;
negative, 8 x 8 cm
The Association of Hungarian
Photographers, Budapest

62
The young Endre Ady 1908-1918
Photograph 29 x 21 cm;
negative, 21 x 16 cm
The Association of Hungarian
Photographers, Budapest

63
The poet Endre Ady, 1908–1918
Photograph 24 x 22 cm;
negative, 24 x 18 cm
The Association of Hungarian
Photographers, Budapest

64**
Léda in Hat, 1908–1918
Photograph 29 x 21.5 cm;
negative, 24 x 18 cm
The Association of Hungarian
Photographers, Budapest

POSTERS

BARDÓCZ, Árpád (1882–1938)

Bardócz was a painter and graphic artist. He studied at the College of Applied Arts, and toured Germany, France, Holland and Norway. Between 1911 and 1913 he did illustrations for a publication entitled *Politikai Magyarország* (Political Hungary). He had a number of exhibitions in the National Salon, and in 1934 worked in Egypt where he painted the murals of the hospital at Al Mo-assed.

65
Elkán Gyula, Furrier, undated
Poster: Budapest, Kellner and Mohrlüder Press
88 x 63 cm
National Széchenyi Library, Budapest

BIRÓ, Mihály (1886–1948)

A painter, graphic artist and sculptor, Biró studied in Budapest at the College of Applied Arts and subsequently in Berlin, Paris and London. In 1910 he won a prize in a poster competition for *The Studio* magazine. He drew attention in Hungary with his Socialist propaganda posters, and in 1912–1913 exhibited at the Arts Centre, then in 1917 at the Ernst Museum. He participated in the revolutionary movements and became the government commissioner of posters during the Councils' Republic. After the fall of the proletarian dictatorship he emigrated to Vienna. Escaping from Nazi expansion he moved to Paris, and returned to Hungary in 1945. His graphic, passionate style and revolutionary themes made him a forerunner of the new Socialist painting.

66
Let's go to the Edison Movie, early 1900s
Poster: Budapest, Seidner's Press, 124 x 93 cm
National Széchenyi Library, Budapest

67**
Palma Rubber heel, ca. 1910
Poster: Budapest, Athenaeum's Press,
95 x 63 cm
Museum of Commerce and the Catering Trade, Budapest

68
The Dáma Woman Decorations, early 1900s
Poster: Budapest, Seidner's Press, 126 x 95 cm
Museum of Commerce and the Catering Trade, Budapest

FARAGÓ, Géza (1877–1928)

A painter, graphic and applied artist, Faragó studied in Paris. Returning to Hungary he found fame mainly through his original and imaginative posters. Around 1910 he worked at the artists' colony at Kecskemét. He drew cartoons and designed decor and costumes for the theatres of the capital. He had several exhibitions at the National Salon.

69**
No danger of fire! Rops spirit-lamp; if it tumbles, it goes out, early 1900s
Poster: Budapest, Seidner's Press, 95 x 62 cm
National Széchenyi Library, Budapest

70
Lipik first class spa, Slavonia, early 1900s
Poster: Budapest, Seidner's Press, 95 x 64 cm
National Széchenyi Library, Budapest

71**
Tungsram, early 1900s
Poster: unknown press, 93 x 62 cm
National Széchenyi Library, Budapest

72
Janina Cigarette paper, ca. 1910
Poster: Koppe-Bellmann's Press, 95 x 63 cm
Museum of Commerce and the Catering Trade, Budapest

67

73
Poster for a Géza Faragó exhibition
in the National Salon, early 1900s
Budapest, Seidner's Press,
96 x 62 cm
National Széchenyi Library,
Budapest

FÖLDES, Imre (b. 1881)

A painter and graphic artist, Földes
studied in Budapest, Vienna, Berlin
and Paris. He produced mainly decorative pictures and posters. From
1918 he ran an independent institute
of graphics in Budapest. In 1921 he
became the art director of the Helikon
of Temesvár, Timisoara, and in 1935
settled down in Bucharest.

74
Dido Cosmetics, no date
Poster: Földes-Sátori and Reményi
Company,

126 x 89 cm
Museum of Commerce and the
Catering Trade, Budapest

HORTI, Pál (see Architecture)

75
Poster for an exhibition of
furnishings, held by the Hungarian
Society for Applied Arts, ca. 1900
Budapest, Ullman József's Press,
95 x 63 cm
National Széchenyi Library,
Budapest

VASZARY, János (see Graphics)

76**
Poster for the Spring International
Exhibition of the Hungarian
National Society for Fine Arts, 1899
Budapest, Kunossy and Sons Press,
96 x 64 cm
National Széchenyi Library,
Budapest

69

71

76

BOOKS AND BOOKPLATES

77

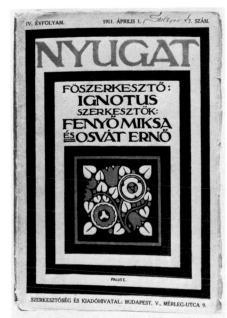

82

BIRÓ, Mihály (see Posters)

77**
Aurora; frontispiece for the *Literary and Artistic Weekly*, 27 May 1911
Jókai Press,
27.5 cm high
Petőfi Literary Museum, Budapest

FALUS, Elek (1884–1950)

A graphic artist and designer Falus studied at Nagybánya and subsequently worked at Szolnok and in Munich. From 1904 he participated in various exhibitions; his work at this time was in the Art Nouveau style. He was a pioneer in the field of Hungarian graphics and book illustration, and after 1910 managed a carpet weaving workshop at Kecskemét. He created the interiors for the Ernst Museum. After 1920 he mainly designed exhibition pavilions.

78
Frontispiece for *New Poems*, by Endre Ady, Budapest, 1912
Edition Pallas,
21 cm high
Petőfi Literary Museum, Budapest

79
Frontispiece for *The Youth of Szindbád* by Gyula Krudy, Budapest, 1912
Edition Nyugat,
21 cm high
Petőfi Literary Museum, Budapest

80
Frontispiece for *Sári biró* Zsigmond Móricz (Judge Sári), Budapest, 1910
Edition Nyugat,
21 cm high
Petőfi Literary Museum, Budapest

81
Frontispiece for *Serenade at Dawn* by Árpád Tóth, Budapest, 1913
Edition Nyugat,
21 cm high
Petőfi Literary Museum, Budapest

82**
Frontispiece for *Nyugat*, periodical, 1 April 1911
27 cm high

Petőfi Literary Museum, Budapest

GARA, Arnold (1882–1929)

A painter, graphic and applied artist, Gara studied at Nagybánya and in Germany. Besides painting in oils he did etchings, posters, book ornaments and illustrations, painted vessels and designed jewelry. In 1926 his album of etchings entitled *Magyar Parnasszus* (Hungarian Parnassus), was published in which he made illustrations to poems by modern Hungarian poets. He had several exhibitions in Hungary as well as abroad.

83**
Rosa Braun's bookplate, 1903
Etching,
14.2 x 10.2 cm; signed: Gara Arnold
Museum of Applied Arts, Budapest

GULÁCSY, Lajos (1882–1932)

Gulácsy was a painter and graphic artist, who began his studies in Budapest at the school of Decorative Arts and then in Rome and Florence. In 1906 he went to Paris. In 1907 there was an exhibition of his work in Budapest at the Urania gallery. In 1914 he was committed to a mental institution where he worked until he became blind. His art is characterized by a curious dream-world and a peculiar lyricism. His work does not belong to any school, but he may be considered a follower of the English Pre-Raphaelites. In 1942 a retrospective exhibition was arranged at the Ernst Museum, and commemorative exhibitions were held in 1936 and 1947. His pictures are in the National Gallery and in private collections.

84
Frontispiece for *Stanzas by the Hooded Painter* by Artur Keleti, Budapest, 1912
Edition Benkő; Jókai Press,
17 cm high
Petőfi Literary Museum, Budapest

85**
Frontispiece for *The Lambs of God*

by Lajos Kassák, Budapest, 1914
Edition Benkő Grill,
18 cm high
Petőfi Literary Museum, Budapest

KOZMA, Lajos (see Architecture)

86
Emil Agoston's bookplate, early
1900s
Cliché after wash-drawing,
9.8 x 6.5 cm; signed: K
Museum of Applied Arts, Budapest

87**
Ilona Kozma's bookplate, early 1900s
Cliché after wash-drawing,
9 x 6.6 cm; signed: K
Museum of Applied Arts, Budapest

88
Ede Földes's bookplate, early 1900s
Cliché after wash-drawing,
11.3 x 5.5 cm; signed: K
Museum of Applied Arts, Budapest

89
Henrik Sipos' bookplate, early 1900s
Cliché after wash-drawing,
9 x 7.2 cm; signed: K
Museum of Applied Arts, Budapest

LESZNAI, Anna (1885–1966)

A writer, graphic and applied artist,
Lesznai became known for her decorative embroidery in the Art Nouveau
style, utilizing elements from Hungarian folk art. In 1911 she participated
in the Group of Eight exhibition, and
in 1932 she had a one-woman show at
the Ernst Museum. From the end of
the 1930s she lived and taught in the
United States. There were commemorative exhibitions of her work in
1975 at Hatvan, and in 1976 at the
National Gallery.

83

90**
Frontispiece for Anna Lesznai's own
book, *Ghost Poems*, Budapest, 1909
Edition Nyugat; Jókai Press,
21 cm high
Petőfi Literary Museum, Budapest

91**
Frontispiece for *Who has seen me?*
by Endre Ady, Budapest, 1914
Edition Nyugat,
21 cm high
Petőfi Literary Museum, Budapest

NAGY, Sándor (see Graphics)

92
Elek Koronghi-Lippich's bookplate,
early 1900s
Woodcut,
9 x 6.5 cm; signed: N S and Morelli G
Museum of Applied Arts, Budapest

93
Károly Lyka's bookplate, early 1900s
Cliché after wash-drawing,
6.2 x 5.2 cm; signed: N S
Museum of Applied Arts, Budapest

94**
Viktor Hornyánszky's bookplate,
early 1900s
3-color print,
14.5 x 6.5 cm; unsigned
Museum of Applied Arts, Budapest

SASSY, Attila (1880–1967)

A painter and graphic artist, Sassy
studied in Budapest, Munich and
Paris. He published his decorative
drawings under the pseudonym L'Aiglon. He participated in a number of
exhibitions; one of his paintings is in
the National Gallery.

95
Frontispiece of book by Margit Kaffka,
Budapest, 1906

87

Edition Athenaeum,
21 cm high
Petőfi Literary Museum, Budapest

96**
Dr. Sándor Konek's bookplate, early
1900s
Cliché after wash-drawing,
11 x 5.7 cm; signed: Aiglon
Museum of Applied Arts, Budapest

97
Dr. Gyula Kenczler's bookplate, early
1900s
Cliché after wash-drawing,

85

90

9.8 x 8.4 cm; signed: Aiglon
Museum of Applied Arts, Budapest

98
Jolán Jemnitz's bookplate, early
1900s
Cliché after wash-drawing,
7.7 x 7 cm; signed: Aiglon
Museum of Applied Arts, Budapest

99
Kálmánné Harsányi's bookplate,
early 1900s
Cliché after wash-drawing,
10.8 x 4.4 cm; signed: Aiglon
Museum of Applied Arts, Budapest

TEVAN, Andor (1889–1955)

A book designer, Tevan studied at the
College of Graphics in Vienna. After
completing his studies he founded, in
1911, the Tevan Library, and published a number of progressive and
foreign-language books. This activity
was followed by the Tevan Amateur
Series. His volumes are among the
outstanding products of modern Hungarian book design.

100
I Start for the North by Zoltán
Somlyó, Békéscsaba, 1912
Edition Tevan,
19 cm high
Petőfi Literary Museum, Budapest

101
New Poems by Gyula Juhász,
Békéscsaba, 1914
Tevan Library,
19 cm high
Petőfi Library Museum, Budapest

94

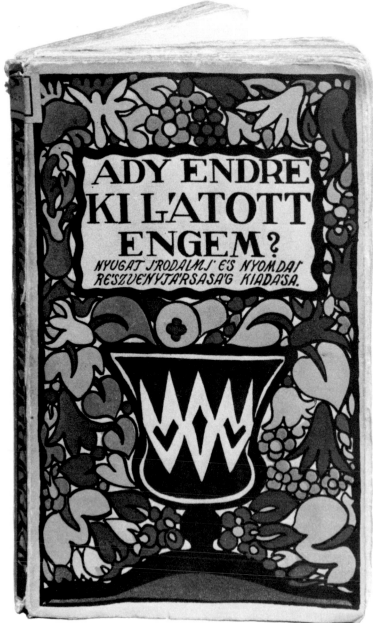

91

96

MERCANTILE GRAPHICS

104

106

A.R. or F.R.

102
Menu-card, 1912
Budapest, Károly's Press,
19.7 x 10.5 cm
Museum of Commerce and the
Catering Trade, Budapest

BARDÓCZ, Árpád (see Posters)

103
Elkan's Furrier, Budapest
Brucksteiner and Sons Press,
Invoice form, 13.5 x 7 cm
Museum of Commerce and the
Catering Trade, Budapest

DARILEK, Henrik (1879–?)

A designer and painter, Darilek, after
completing his studies at the College
of Applied Arts, was employed at the
Zsolnay factory at Pécs between 1898
and 1906. In 1906 he moved to
Budapest and worked as a designer
and interior decorator.

104**
Invitation card for the Joiners' Craft
Union ball in Budapest, 1913
Color print,
16.5 x 26.8 cm
Museum of Applied Arts, Budapest

105
Chocolat au lait, 1910
Color packaging,
15 x 19.7 cm
Museum of Applied Arts, Budapest

106**
Pastilles de chocolat, 1910
Color packaging,
14 x 15.8 cm
Museum of Applied Arts, Budapest

107
Chocolat Gourmand, 1910
Color packaging
14.8 x 19.5 cm
Museum of Applied Arts, Budapest

108
Chocolat aux amandes (Almond
chocolate), 1910
Color packaging,
15 x 20 cm
Museum of Applied Arts, Budapest

109
Confiserie Globus, Budapest, 1910

111

TÖRLEY

BUDAPEST-
BUDAFOK

KUNOSSY MŰINTEZET BUDAPEST

112

Color packaging,
21.2 x 31.5 cm
Museum of Applied Arts, Budapest

DIVÉKY, József (see Graphics)

110
Hotel English Queen
Lehár's birthday party, 1914
Budapest, unknown press,
Menu card, 16.3 x 12.6 cm
Museum of Commerce and the
Catering Trade, Budapest

FARAGÓ, Géza (see Posters)

111**
Holzer's Fashion Store
Budapest, Lengyel Lipót's Press,
Invoice form, 13.5 x 6.9 cm
Museum of Commerce and the
Catering Trade, Budapest

112**
Törley Champagne
Budapest, Kunossy Institute,
Invoice form, 6.7 x 13.3 cm
Museum of Commerce and the
Catering Trade, Budapest

113
Mineral water of Szántó
Budapest, Bakács's Lithography,
Invoice form, 7.4 x 13.3 cm
Museum of Commerce and the
Catering Trade, Budapest

N.S. or S.N.

114
Margaret Island, International
Congress of Hotel-keepers, no date
Budapest, Czettel and Deutsch's
Press,
Menu card, 25.8 x 35 cm
Museum of Commerce and the
Catering Trade, Budapest

Designer unknown

115
Arany Bika (Golden Bull) Hotel,
Debrecen, ca. 1910
Budapest, Munk and Balog's Press,
Menu card, 33.3 x 20.5 cm
Museum of Commerce and the
Catering Trade, Budapest

Designer unknown

116
Gizella settlement, rest-house and
bath
Budapest, Rigler Company,
Invoice form, 7.7 x 14 cm
Museum of Commerce and the
Catering Trade, Budapest

117
Páskuj, Imre
Budapest, Posner's Press,
7.5 x 14.5 cm
Museum of Commerce and the
Catering Trade, Budapest

118
Lily Linen Company
6.2 x 14.1 cm
Museum of Commerce and the
Catering Trade, Budapest

119
Weszely's Sports Equipment
Budapest, Globus Institute,
7.2 x 14.5 cm
Museum of Commerce and the
Catering Trade, Budapest

120
Kossák József's Photography
7.3 x 14.1 cm
Museum of Commerce and the
Catering Trade, Budapest

121
Schulcz Stationery, Léva
14.9 x 7.7 cm
Museum of Commerce and the
Catering Trade, Budapest

122
Prince Windisch-Graetz-type of Tokaj
wines
Budapest,
14.4 x 7 cm
Museum of Commerce and the
Catering Trade, Budapest

123
Littke Champagne
Budapest, Gy. Klösz and Sons Press,
13.8 x 7 cm
Museum of Commerce and the
Catering Trade, Budapest

124
Dományi's Rock Wine, Arad
Budapest, Athenaeum,
13.7 x 6 cm
Museum of Commerce and the
Catering Trade, Budapest

125
Réthy's Horehound Sweets,
Békéscsaba
Warnsdorf, E. Straché's Press,
15.7 x 7.6 cm
Museum of Commerce and the
Catering Trade, Budapest

126**
Stollwerck (toffee),
7 x 14 cm
Museum of Commerce and the
Catering Trade, Budapest

127
Rosenberg's Silk, Linen, Budapest,
15 x 8.6 cm
Museum of Commerce and the
Catering Trade, Budapest

PACKAGING

Designers unknown

128
Reiter Izsó's Sweet Red Pepper box,
ca. 1910
Sheet iron,
19 x 19 x 26 cm

Museum of Commerce and the
Catering Trade, Budapest

129
Reiter Izsó's Red Pepper shaker, ca.
1900
Sheet iron,
9.8 x 4 cm diameter
Museum of Commerce and the
Catering Trade, Budapest

130
Princesas Cigarette box, 1900–10
Sheet iron,
9 x 8 x 1.6 cm
Museum of Commerce and the
Catering Trade, Budapest

131**
Box with *Hattyu Email* (Swan
enamel) inscription, ca. 1910
Sheet iron (lid missing),
9.7 x 7.5 cm diameter
Museum of Commerce and the
Catering Trade, Budapest

132**
Schmidl's Cocoa box, 1900–10
Sheet iron,
20.5 x 20 x 31.5 cm
Museum of Commerce and the
Catering Trade, Budapest

126

131

132

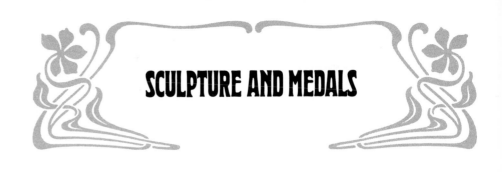

SCULPTURE AND MEDALS

135

140

BECK Ö., Fülöp (1873–1945)

A sculptor and medallist, Beck was one of the pioneers of modern Hungarian sculpture. He began his studies at the College of Applied Arts in the hope of becoming a goldsmith. In 1893 he went to Paris on a scholarship, and in 1895 won first prize at the Millenary Exhibition's medal-design competition. He returned and settled down in Budapest. His powerful reliefs in tight form and the serenity of his figures lend him a role in Hungarian sculpture similar to that of Maillol. His work is in the collection of the National Gallery.

133
Kurutz Head, relief, 1913
Bronze relief,
36 x 24 cm
Hungarian National Gallery,
Budapest

134
Korányi Frigyes, 1901
Bronze, struck coin,
7 cm diameter
Hungarian National Gallery,
Budapest

135**
String Quartet, 1914
Bronze, struck plaque,
6.5 x 8.5 cm
Hungarian National Gallery,
Budapest

136
Miklós Zsolnay, reverse, 1907
Bronze, struck plaque,
5.9 x 8.5 cm
Hungarian National Gallery,
Budapest

137
Sándor Petőfi, reverse, 1905
Bronze, struck plaque,
4.9 x 7.1 cm
Hungarian National Gallery,
Budapest

138
Photo Club, 1903
Bronze, struck plaque,
4.8 x 4.2 cm
Hungarian National Gallery,
Budapest

139
Pál Gyulai, 1906
Bronze, struck plaque,
7.4 x 7.7 cm
Hungarian National Gallery,
Budapest

BERÁN, Lajos (1882–1943)

Béran was a sculptor and medalist who studied in Budapest and then at the Academy of Vienna. He was chief engraver of the Hungarian National Mint, and one of Hungary's most active medalists. Examples of his work are in the medal and sculpture collection of the National Gallery.

140**
Mrs György Ráth, 1914
Bronze plaque,
14 x 7 cm
Hungarian National Gallery,
Budapest

141
Sándor Kőrösi Csoma, reverse, 1909
Bronze, struck medal,
6 cm diameter
Hungarian National Gallery,
Budapest

FÉMES BECK, Vilmos (1885–1918)

A designer and sculptor, Fémes Beck studied at the School of Applied Arts. In 1906 he won a gold medal at the International Exhibition in Milan. He pursued his studies in Darmstadt, Munich, Paris, and London, and upon returning to Hungary his plaques clearly showed the impact of early

143

Renaissance medals. Later he was attracted to the Group of Eight and became preoccupied with modern plastics. His work is in the collections of the National Gallery and the Museum of Applied Arts.

142
Dancer, 1905
Bronze statuette,
30.5 cm high
Hungarian National Gallery,
Budapest

143**
For the Goddess of Visual Pleasures,
undated
Bronze medal,
7.4 cm diameter
Hungarian National Gallery,
Budapest

144
Kneeling Female Nude, 1911
Bronze, struck coin,
5.3 cm diameter
Hungarian National Gallery,
Budapest

FERENCZY, Béni (1890–1967)

A sculptor, graphic artist and teacher, Ferenczy was awarded the Kossuth prize and the title "Eminent Artist", and became one of the most prominent figures in Hungarian arts. He studied in Florence, Munich and Paris: worked with Bourdelle in 1911, and with Archipenko in 1912. After 1919 he emigrated and lived in Vienna, Berlin and then in Moscow, returning to Hungary in 1935. In his early career he was preoccupied with Cubism, but from the 1920s his work was influenced by classical art. His statues are characterized by a mastery of composition and sensitive modeling. He also wrote on the arts. His work is in the collection of the National Gallery.

145

148

146

145**
Girl's Head: Noémi, 1917
Bronze statuette,
33 cm high
Hungarian National Gallery,
Budapest

KISFALUDI STROBL, Zsigmond
(1884–1975)

Sculptor and winner of the Kossuth prize and title of "Eminent Artist," Kisfaludi Strobl studied at the School of Applied Arts, at the Master School for Sculptors, and later in Vienna and Paris. After the First World War he was very successful; fulfilling countless commissions. His work is vivid and expressive, moderately psychologizing the model and full of motion. He was a many-sided and versatile artist, creating portraits, nudes, small plastics and memorials: his bust of George Bernard Shaw is outstanding. Almost 50 of his statues are erected in Hungary, and many are abroad, for instance, his *Birth of Venus* in California. A large number of his works are in public collections in Hungary and abroad.

146**
Finale, 1911
Bronze statuette,
50 cm high
Hungarian National Gallery,
Budapest

LÁNYI, Dezső (1879–1951)

A sculptor, Dezső Lányi studied in Budapest, Vienna, Paris and Brussels, and began exhibiting in 1904. He worked in portraits, genre-scenes, statues and memorial monuments; some examples are in the collection of the National Gallery. From the 1930s onward he lived in the United States.

147
Léda and the Swan, 1912
Bronze statuette,
45 cm high
Hungarian National Gallery,
Budapest

MOIRET, Ödön (1883–1966)

A sculptor, architect and medalist, Moiret studied in Budapest, Vienna and Brussels. Between 1911 and 1919 he taught sculpture at the Technical University of Budapest. During these years he also worked at the artists' colony in Gödöllő. His early sculpture was heavily symbolic, but in the 1930s he turned to the spirit of the 20th century. Several of his works are in the collection of the National Gallery. His statues may also be found in Vienna, Hanover, Berlin, and in foreign museum collections.

148**
St George, 1911
Silver, struck plaque,
7.95 x 5.95 cm
Hungarian National Gallery,
Budapest

REMÉNYI, József (b. 1887)

Reményi was a sculptor and medalist
who studied in Budapest and Munich.
From 1927 until 1944 he taught at the
School of Applied Arts; between 1943
and 1948 he was the art director of the
Hungarian National Mint. His works
are characterized by clear composition, technical perfection and a classi-
cist approach. His medals are richly
represented in the Hungarian National Museum and in the National
Gallery. In 1972 the Hungarian National Gallery organized a retrospective exhibition.

149
Kalotaszeg, 1908
Bronze, struck plaque,
7.05 x 4.8 cm
Hungarian National Gallery,
Budapest

SIMAY, Imre (1874–1955)

A sculptor, painter and graphic artist,
Simay studied in Vienna and Munich.
He sculpted animal figures in a strong
Cubist style, concentrating his blocky
forms and avoiding unnecessary detail. He taught sculpture and figure
drawing at the School of Applied Arts.
His early and most significant pieces
are in the National Gallery collection.

150**
Family Joy, 1904
Bronze statuette,
30 cm high
Hungarian National Gallery,
Budapest

TELCS, Ede (1872–1948)

Telcs was a sculptor who studied in
Vienna. Of his many-sided activities,
his small terracotta statues were the
most popular. Several sculptures by
him were erected in Budapest and
some country towns. However,
throughout his life his main preoccu-
pation was with medal art, and he
educated a whole generation of
medalists. He participated in a
number of exhibitions and won prizes
at home and abroad.

151**
Rosemary, 1900
Tin relief in wooden frame,
27.5 x 27 cm
Hungarian National Gallery,
Budapest

152
Girls' Association of Budapest, 1909
Bronze, struck coin,
3.6 cm diameter
Hungarian National Gallery,
Budapest

150

151

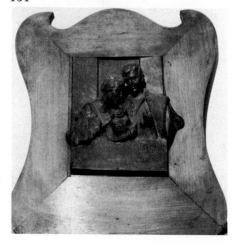

METALWORK

154

155

BECK, Ö. Fülöp (see Sculptures)

153**
Jug, 1898
Bronze,
17 cm high
Signed: BÖF
Museum of Applied Arts, Budapest

154**
Candlestick, 1898
Bronze,
26.5 cm high
Museum of Applied Arts, Budapest

155**
Plate, 1898
Bronze,
25 cm diameter (with handles)
Signed: BÖF
Museum of Applied Arts, Budapest

156
Plate, ca. 1900
Bronze,
19 cm diameter
Museum of Applied Arts, Budapest

157**
Vase, ca. 1900
Bronze,
17.5 x 9.2 cm diameter
Museum of Applied Arts, Budapest

158
Ornamental plate, ca. 1900
Tin,
1.5 x 19.1 cm diameter
Museum of Applied Arts, Budapest

159
Cup, ca. 1900
Bronze,
6.8 x 18 cm diameter
Museum of Applied Arts, Budapest

HORTI, Pál (see Architecture)

160
Bracelet in five parts, ca. 1900
Silver gilt, with green cloisonné,
2 x 16 cm
Museum of Applied Arts, Budapest

153

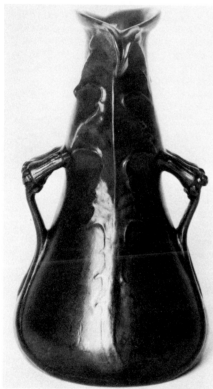

157

161
Pendant, before 1902
Ceramic in silver gilt setting, with
eosin beads,
3.4 x 2.2 cm
Made at the Zsolnay pottery
Museum of Applied Arts, Budapest

HUBER TRAJÁN, Oszkár
(1875–1933)

A silversmith and sculptor, Tarján
studied in Budapest, Munich and
subsequently in Paris at Lalique. He
created chiefly eclesiastical objects,
and his early works bear the impress
of ecclecticism and historicism.
From the turn of the century his
work was characterized by Art
Nouveau, and its influences. From
his *oeuvre* the jewelry made with
transparent enamel is now
considered the most important.

162**
Comb, ca. 1900
Horn, engraved with gold and opals,
10.5 x 5.4 cm
Museum of Applied Arts, Budapest

163**
Pendant, ca. 1902
Silver, with multi-color glazes,
5.2 x 6.5 cm diameter
Museum of Applied Arts, Budapest

164
Pendant, 1900
Silvergilt, with amethyst and
multi-color cloisonné,
6.2 x 6.5 cm
Museum of Applied Arts, Budapest

Designer unknown:

165**
Table lamp, ca. 1900
Brass,
32 x 45 cm
Museum of Applied Arts, Budapest

165

162

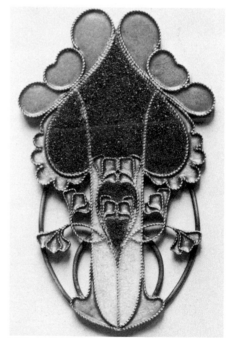

163

CERAMICS

166

APATI ABT, Sándor (1870–1916)

A sculptor and ceramist, Apati Abt studied in Budapest and Munich. He worked at the Zsolnay factory, Pécs, as a designer, and then as a teacher at Székesfehérvár. He was one of the pioneers of modern Hungarian ceramic art.

166**
Vase, 1902
Faience, with *eosin* glaze,
37 cm high
Marked: Zsolnay; signed: ABT
Museum of Applied Arts, Budapest

MACK, Lajos

167**
Vase, 1899
Ceramic with red glaze,
38 cm high
Marked: Zsolnay; signed ML
Museum of Applied Arts, Budapest

NIKELSZKY, Géza (1877-1966)

A painter and applied artist, Nikelszky studied at the School of Applied Arts in Budapest and in Munich. In 1899 he settled down in Pécs, and was a designer at the Zsolnay factory for 52 years. He had several exhibitions in Budapest and Pécs, and his ceramics are in the collections of the Museum of Applied Arts and in the Janus Pannonius Museum at Pécs; where some of his watercolors may also be seen.

168
Vase, 1904
Faience, with *eosin* glaze,
20.5 cm high
Marked: Zsolnay; signed: NG
Museum of Applied Arts, Budapest

RIPPL-RÓNAI, József (see Graphics)

169
Wall-plaque, 1897
Painted faience,
17.5 x 17.5 cm
Made in France; signed: RR
Museum of Applied Arts, Budapest

ZSOLNAY CERAMIC WORKS

The Zsolnay Ceramic Works was founded in 1851 when Miklós ZSOLNAY, Sr, a merchant, bought the equipment of the tile factory at Lukafa and had it set up in Pécs. His eldest son, Ignác, learned the trade at Lukafa. At first the factory manufactured simple clay products, glazed art pottery and decorative ornaments for buildings. In 1863 Ignác handed down the factory to his younger brother Vilmos. Under Vilmos Zsolnay (1828–1900) it developed into a modern factory, which he managed from 1872 until his death. In 1873 Zsolnay stepped into the international limelight at the International Exhibition in Vienna, and in 1878 won unanimous praise with his *"porcelaine faience"* and his decorative vessels as refined as jewels. Around 1890 Zsolnay invented cold-resisting pyrogranite, which has found world-wide use as a ceramic substance in architecture. In 1893, based on the experiments of Vince Wartha, he created a new variant on metallic glazes and called it *eosin*. His whole family participated in the factory. After his death, the ornament and mosaics for the Gellért public baths in Budapest were made. In 1948 the factory was nationalized, and after a brief interval the artistic division started up again and has been functioning ever since.

Designers unknown:

170**
Vase, 1900
Faience, with *eosin* glaze,
34 cm high
Marked: Zsolnay
Museum of Applied Arts, Budapest

171
Vase, ca. 1900
Grès, with *eosin* glaze,
28 cm high
Marked: Zsolnay
Museum of Applied Arts, Budapest

177

167

170

172
Vase, ca. 1900
Stoneware, with *eosin* glaze,
34.3 cm high
Marked: Zsolnay
Museum of Applied Arts, Budapest

173
Vase, ca. 1900
Faience, with *eosin* glaze,
21 cm high
Marked: Zsolnay
Museum of Applied Arts, Budapest

174
Vase, ca. 1902
Porcelaine faience,
25 cm high
Marked: Zsolnay
Museum of Applied Arts, Budapest

175
Vase, ca. 1903
Faience, with *eosin* glaze,
28.8 cm high
Marked: Zsolnay
Museum of Applied Arts, Budapest

176
Vase, ca. 1905
Ironstone, glazed,

29.5 cm high
Marked: Zsolnay
Museum of Applied Arts, Budapest

177**
Ornamental plate, ca. 1905
Porcelaine faience, with *eosin*
glaze,
15.5 x 34.1 cm
Marked: Zsolnay
Museum of Applied Arts, Budapest

178
Wall-tile, ca. 1908
Ceramic, with *eosin* glaze,
15.5 x 15.3 cm
Museum of Applied Arts, Budapest

179
Wall-tile, ca. 1900
Ceramic with *eosin* glaze,
15.2 x 15.2 cm
Marked: Zsolnay
Museum of Applied Arts, Budapest

180
Wall-tile, ca. 1900
Ceramic, with *eosin* glaze,
15.3 x 15.3 cm
Marked: Zsolnay
Museum of Applied Arts, Budapest

GLASS

181

RÓTH, Miksa (1865–1944)

A glass painter and glass mosaicist, Róth had a rather important role in the history of Hungarian decorative glass. He set up his workshop in 1885 and produced glass pieces for the public buildings of a quickly developing Budapest for several decades. He executed the glass ceiling for the National Theatre of Mexico. To his credit he always fought for the preservation of the characteristics of glass as a material, and for the reestablishment of its style following medieval traditions.

181**
Glass window, ca. 1896–97
Opalescent glass in tin frame,
61.5 x 43 cm
Museum of Applied Arts, Budapest

182
Stained-glass window, ca. 1896–97
Opalescent glass in tin frame,
61.5 x 43 cm
Museum of Applied Arts, Budapest

183
Mirror in frame, ca. 1900
Opalescent glass, with metal frame,
24.5 x 32 cm
Museum of Applied Arts, Budapest

SOVÁNKA, István (1858–1945?)

A wood-carver and glassmaker, Sovánka studied at the wood-carvers' school in Zayugróc between 1875 and 1880. Later he worked as a sculptor and, subsequently changing his career, he became the master of layered, colored glass hyalography at the glass factory in Zay-Ugrócz (now Uhrovec). He won a number of prizes with his works, some of which are in the Museum of Applied Arts.

186-187

184**
Vase, ca. 1900
Layered, corroded glass,
21.5 cm high; signed: Sovánka
Museum of Applied Arts, Budapest

185
Vase, ca. 1900
Layered, corroded glass,
26.7 cm high; signed: Sovánka
Museum of Applied Arts, Budapest

SCHREIBER's Glassworks,
Zay-Ugrócz (now Uhrovec)

The glassworks founded by János Schreiber and a family relative was an important source of Art Nouveau objects at the turn of the century. His engraved and milled dishes decorated with Hungarian motifs were very successful at the Paris International Exhibition in 1900

186**
Decanter with cork, ca. 1900
Iridescent transparent glass,
28.5 cm high
Museum of Applied Arts, Budapest

187**
Stemmed glass, ca. 1900
16 cm high
Museum of Applied Arts, Budapest

184

LEATHER WORK

188   189

GOTTERMAYER, Nándor (ca. 1850–1924)

Gottermayer was the manager of the most important leather workshop in Hungary at the turn of the century. His bookcovers and picture frames were richly decorated with Art Nouveau ornament.

188**
Album, ca. 1898
Leather inlay,
22 x 17 cm; signed: Gottermayer N.
Museum of Applied Arts, Budapest

189**
Picture frame, ca. 1900
Parchment and gilt,
33 x 26 cm; signed: Gottermayer N.
Museum of Applied Arts, Budapest

JASCHIK, Álmos (1885–1950)

A graphic artist, teacher and writer, Jaschik studied in Budapest. He began as a book illustrator under the influence of Art Nouveau, and then between 1907 and 1920, he taught at the School of Industrial Drawing. After 1920 he ran a progressive private school. From 1935 he designed stage sets and costumes for the National Theatre. He also wrote books on art.

190
Book-binding, *The Art of Life* by Pál Nádai, 1914
Painted calf-skin, with cut and gilt ornament,
17 x 10.5 x 1.8 cm
Signed: Book-bindery of the Budapest Design School, made by teacher Jaschik
Museum of Applied Arts, Budapest

NAGY, Sándor (see Graphics)

Sándor Nagy collaborated with Leo Belmonte, a Swedish painter and designer. Belmonte studied in Paris at the Académie Julian and at the Manufacture de Gobelins. In 1904, on the invitation of Aladár Kőrösfői Kriesch, he went to Gödöllő and helped set up the weaving school and workshop. He worked in the Gobelin manner, executing cartoons by Kőrösfői-Kriesch and Nagy, but designing independently as well. In 1914 he returned to Paris.

191**
Folding screen, ca. 1900
Painted and cut calf-skin,
49.4 x 74 cm
Signed: SNL, BL
Museum of Applied Arts, Budapest

192**
Writing-pad, ca. 1900
Painted and cut calf-skin,
39 x 29 cm; signed: SNL
Museum of Applied Arts, Budapest

193
Wallet, ca. 1900
Calf-skin with cut ornament,
13.2 x 7.7 cm
Signed: SNL, BL
Museum of Applied Arts, Budapest

194**
Bible, ca. 1900
Pierced leather binding,
24.8 x 16 x 5.7 cm
Signed: SNL, BL
Museum of Applied Arts, Budapest

195**
Writing-pad, ca. 1900
Cut calf-skin, with braiding,
22 x 14 cm

191

192

194

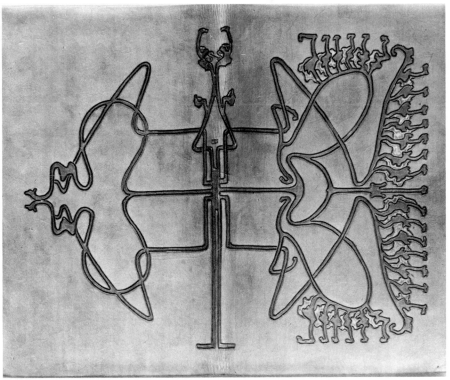

195

197

Signed: SNL, BL
Museum of Applied Arts, Budapest
196
Picture frame, ca. 1900
Painted and cut calf-skin,
22.5 x 21 cm
Signed: SNL, BL
Museum of Applied Arts, Budapest

NÁDLER, Róbert (1858–1938)

Nádler was a painter who studied architecture and later chose to return to painting. He worked for two years in Vienna, and from 1889 taught at the School of Decorative Arts. In 1915 he became the dean of the School of Applied Arts. Between 1917 and 1929 he taught ornamental drawing and folk art at the Technical University. He participated in exhibitions and won prizes for his delicately detailed town scenes and his gay genre pictures painted in a Naturalist style. He made many reforms in the teaching of drawing.

197**
Book-binding: poems by Elek Koronghy-Lippich, 1903 (Illustrated by A. Kőrösfői-Kriesch and S. Nagy)
Calf-skin with batik work,
17.5 x 21.5 cm
Signed: NR
Hungarian National Gallery, Budapest

FASHION

200

Designers unknown:

198
Woman's two-piece costume, early 1900s
Flaxen linen, with braiding and open-work embroidered flowers; skirt length: 110 cm
Museum of Applied Arts, Budapest

199
Shirt front, early 1900s
Cotton and silk
Museum of Applied Arts, Budapest

200**
Woman's dress, early 1900s
Black lace on yellow silk, embroidered with pearls and flowers; length: 135 cm
Labeled: Maison Grünstein Robes & Confection, Orosháza
Museum of Applied Arts, Budapest

201
Hat, early 1900s
Black straw, with marabou plume, 58 cm diameter
Labeled: Neufeld Samu, Budapest, Dorottya utca 8.
Museum of Applied Arts, Budapest

202
Woman's handbag, early 1900s
Needlework, with colored Venetian pearl,
16.5 x 20 cm
Museum of Applied Arts, Budapest

203
Woman's handbag, early 1900s
Velvet, with metal and ceramic ornament
14 x 17 cm
Museum of Applied Arts, Budapest

204
Parasol, early 1900s
Black lace on white silk,
56 cm long
Museum of Applied Arts, Budapest

205
Fan, early 1900s. Made by Gizella Mirkovszky Greguss
Stained wood, with painted silk cover,
26 cm high
Museum of Applied Arts, Budapest

LACES

DÉKÁNI, Árpád (1865–1931)

A designer and teacher, Dékáni studied in Budapest and then taught at the grammar school in Kiskunhalas, Halas. He collected folk art, and under its influence designed his first lace which soon became internationally known as the "lace of Halas." Around 1900 the needlework-teacher, Mariska Markovits, developed a technique based on his designs. Much of the early lace was multi-colored: a mix of Art Nouveau and Hungarian folk art forms. In 1907 a lacemaking showroom and workshop was set up in Budapest under Dékáni's management, and for a time he taught at the School of Applied Arts and later at the grammar school in Ujpest. In 1918 he gave up his activities and returned to his homeland Transylvania. Halas lace has remained justly famous for six decades.

206
Lace, 1904–11
Colored silks,
12.5 x 37 cm
Lace-making workshop of
Kiskunhalas
Museum of Applied Arts, Budapest

207**
Lace, 1904–11
Colored silks,
17 x 25 cm
Lace-making workshop of
Kiskunhalas
Museum of Applied Arts, Budapest

208
Lace, 1904–11
Colored silks,
8 x 22.5 cm
Lace-making workshop of
Kiskunhalas
Museum of Applied Arts, Budapest

209
Lace, 1904–11
Linen flax,
9.5 x 26 cm
Lace-making workshop of
Kiskunhalas
Museum of Applied Arts, Budapest

210
Lace, 1904–11
Colored silks,
8.5 x 24 cm
Lace-making workshop of
Kiskunhalas
Museum of Applied Arts, Budapest

211
Lace, 1904–11
Colored silks,
7.5 x 26 cm
Lace-making workshop of
Kiskunhalas
Museum of Applied Arts, Budapest

212**
Lace, 1904–11
Colored silks
16 x 42 cm
Lace-making workshop of
Kiskunhalas
Museum of Applied Arts, Budapest

213
Fan Lace, 1909
Flax,
11.5 x 46 cm
Lace-making workshop of
Kiskunhalas
Museum of Applied Arts, Budapest

214**
Lace, 1904–11
Colored silks
12 x 31 cm
Lace-making workshop of
Kiskunhalas
Museum of Applied Arts, Budapest

215**
Fan lace, 1904–11
Colored silks,
21.5 x 44.5 cm
Lace-making workshop of
Kiskunhalas
Museum of Applied Arts, Budapest

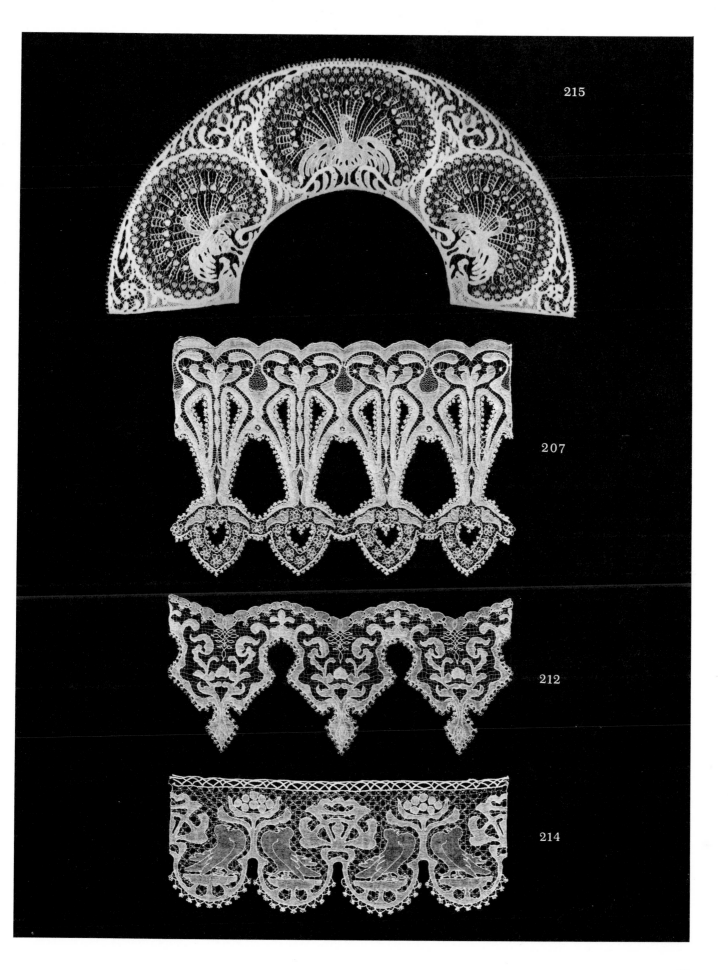

215

207

212

214

TAPESTRIES

216

HORTI, Pál (see Architecture)

216**
Carpet, 1901. Made by Mrs Kabay
Silk, Ghiordes knot, closeness:
7000/Dm²
245 x 165 cm
Signed: K D 1901
Museum of Applied Arts, Budapest

KŐRÖSFŐI-KRIESCH, Aladár
(1863–1920)

A painter, designer and craftsman, Kőrösfői-Kriesch was a characteristic representative of Hungarian Art Nouveau. In Budapest he was the disciple of Bertalan Székely and Károly Lotz, in Munich he studied under Sándor Liezen-Mayer. In 1901, after a study tour in Italy, he settled down at Gödöllő where—with Sándor Nagy—he founded an artists' colony which became the center of Hungarian Art Nouveau. Its members worked together under the impact of the English Pre-Raphaelite movement, and besides the fine arts, they also cultivated several branches of the applied arts. In 1904 he opened a school for weaving at Gödöllő. Here he designed in the manner of Gobelins; he worked also in mosaics and painted frescoes (e.g., the dining hall of the House of Parliament; the frescoes at the Academy of Music). Toward the end of his life he experimented with making sculpture. As well as writing about art, he held a teaching post at the School of Applied Arts from 1907 until 1920. His work is in the National Gallery collection.

217

220

218

217**
Cassandra, 1908
Wool, woven, closeness of warping:
7/cm
200 x 71 cm
Made by Leo Belmonte; signed: BL,
KA
Museum of Applied Arts, Budapest

NAGY, Sándor (see Graphics)

218**
Toldi, ca. 1917
Wool, woven, closeness of warping:
4/cm,
192 x 108 cm
Made by Margit Guillaume; signed:
GM, SNL
Museum of Applied Arts, Budapest

VASZARY, János (see Graphics)

219
Country couple, late 1900s
Wool, woven, closeness of warping:
4/cm,
152 x 116 cm
Made by Sarolta Kovalszky
Museum of Applied Arts, Budapest

220**
At the Fair, late 1900s
Wool, woven, closeness of warping:
4/cm,
152 x 116 cm
Made by Sarolta Kovalszky
Museum of Applied Arts, Budapest

SELECTED ARTICLES ON HUNGARIAN ART NOUVEAU

ENDRE ADY: ART NOUVEAU

And regarding the moral traditions, England was already dead at the end of the nineteenth century. Economic power, which was shared only by a few groups, had become tyrannical and autocratic, depressing the vigour of the population and industrial enterprise. Mercenary wars and retributions had divided the nation. Below the aged Queen there was no court, no landed aristocracy, as the land was spoiled and exhausted. Only one god was worshipped, the golden calf, and only its prophets were the masters. Scandals had become more numerous, luxury and corruption had orgies together with social hypocrisy. In a word, civilization has crowned its work by suppressing the individual, and the English, this manly race, has become stunted. By adapting the customs of the barbarians conquered by them the British Empire has entered the twentieth century with the saddest perspective . . . ."

In *Blackwood Magazine*, the Scottish periodical, this prophecy is expressed by an undoubtedly deep-thinking writer, the imaginary Gibbon of the next century to the people of England.

This image he sees is rather gloomy and disconsolate. It is even more gloomy as the present can give birth only to such a future.

This future is not only of England, but more or less it is the future of all of us. It is ours as well. "Present civilization suppresses the individual." This is stated by the "Gibbon of the future." It is a great truth that lives in every heart—only a few dare express it!

But this truth is the basis of all the problems of the age. The hitherto inevitable social reforms have to start from this:

Because the individual cannot be suppressed for long!

History proves that the bloodiest transformations were due to the individual's efforts for liberation.

The suppressed individual does not make revolution with arms as yet, but he has already started his struggle! For the time being the struggle is conducted on the highest plane: it is in the arts and in literature. The advocates of old barriers jeer at the apostles and misunderstand their objectives, and they totally misunderstand the basis of these objectives. The masses consider it to be a fashion while it is only the first and unassuming advance-guard action of a great universal transformation. So leave Art Nouveau alone all of you who are the puppets of the barriers! Revolution and human beings are fundamental to it and not fashion dolls.

The Gibbon of the next century will look back upon our age from the new, transformed world of Art Nouveau!

Debreceni Newspaper, 19 April 1899.

IGNOTUS: ONCE AGAIN ON ART NOUVEAU

Art is the subjective explanation of the world in contrast to science which explains it objectively. In science there is no room for the individual as scientifically there is only one truth. In art there are as many truths as human beings. If Rippl-Rónai feels like regarding the world garish blue, I can only comment upon the success of the execution. I may criticize the painter but the trend is above my powers. In art all trends are legitimate without any exception. This eternal truth and only this one is advocated by the artistic revolution called Art Nouveau, this eternal law, without the vital power of which art would have petrified somewhere at the Egyptian hieroglyphs without progress and development. All the great masters, all the Raphaels and Rembrandts who are utilized today against Art Nouveau, had grown to immortality because of this law. Rembrandt could have been asked why he had seen the world golden yellow, Michelangelo could have been asked why the world consisted of athletes and hermaphrodites. It could have been explained to Tintoretto that the colors seen by him did not exist

even on the Syrius. It could have been explained to Raphael that the artist should observe real life and the Dutch could have listened to lectures on how each picture is supposed to express an idea . . . .
A Hét (The Week), 1899.

KÁROLY LYKA: ART NOUVEAU STYLE— HUNGARIAN STYLE

We have outlined in brief what has caused at home and abroad the breakaway of innovators from the academics. We have also described what objectives inspire the secessionists at home and abroad, and also how their efforts were received by the public and by the critics at home and abroad. And now we refer to that marked similarity which cannot be misunderstood in the secession of Hungarian and foreign artists. We can see that almost exactly the same happened here as abroad. In other words the origin of Art Nouveau and of the "Hungarian style"—to use a popular term—is the same. And their destiny is also similar, moreover identical, as can be seen by their yet brief career. So, what is generally considered to be the style of Art Nouveau is similar in its origin, essence and effect to what is normally called the Hungarian style. This statement may hurt those who label with the term Art Nouveau all craziness and fads. We have to protest against such an interpretation of the term. And we may not have put down even once the term Art Nouveau in this article, had we not dealt with this question on the occasion of the official ban of the Art Nouveau style. There is less scope for misunderstanding if on the basis of what has been said above, we state that the style sought by Hungarian artists is essentially identical with the efforts of modern foreign artists. In other words these two are in line and cannot be opposed to each other . . . .
Művészet (Art), 1902.

REVIEW IN THE "MISSISSIPPI BLÄTTER" OF THE ST LOUIS EXHIBITION, 1904.

The Hungarian section in the Manufacturers building, which was inaugurated last week, is a new, important and interesting component in the series of exhibitions by foreign nations. The large number of eminent guests were received by Government Commissioner György Szögyény, who is also the American special correspondent for the Royal Hungarian Ministry of Commerce. Among the guests were Dr Lajos Hegyeshalmy, Councilor to the head of the ministerial department, and the prominent representative of the Hungarian Association of Applied Arts, Professor Pál Horti, who is the art and technical manager for the exhibition and designer of the installation. The spirited songs of the excellent gipsy band and the original, characteristic building with its typical ornamentation created the proper atmosphere right at the entrance to the fenced courtyard, and the attractive, inherent amiability of the Hungarians was fully expressed toward the invited guests.

The Hungarian Empire is exhibiting a rich series of its silk products in the Hall of Agriculture, and marble and various kinds of mineral water in the group representing mining, foundry work and metallurgy. In the Hall of Arts are displayed several works by eminent Hungarian artists, who did not build a separate pavilion. Yet, the fenced section, surrounded by walls, turrets and windows, with its broad foreground, spacious hall and four or five apartments for the Hungarians in the Manufacturers building creates the impression of a peculiar Hungarian manor. It cannot be regarded as a harmonious whole as the outer part, with its 14th-century green wooden fence, the lateral passages covered with red tile, the four high towers in the four corners each surrounded by four smaller turrets, brought together by a pointed gate in the center, represent a typical "Székely", i.e.: Transylvanian manorial house, where a richly ornamented wrought iron gate leads to the central part as if to a baronial palace. This is the *piece de resistance* of the ensemble made by Forreider and Schiller, the two well-known ironsmiths from Budapest. Here, besides two sets of furniture done in a rather popular style, there are several sets of luxury furniture, indicating that the objective was to present the widest possible image of the various branches of Hungarian applied arts in the limited space.

The exterior of the manor built after the designs of Professor Horti, which creates an open courtyard with large show cases and shop windows, is totally in keeping with its original character, and the effect is further enhanced by the large mural by Aladár Kriesch, representing the people of Kalotaszeg going to church in their picturesquely colorful garments. The outer wooden fence, the large Székely gate in the middle, and the four towers were made by the Gregersen & Sons Company of Budapest. The imposing iron gate of the inner entrance has already found its American owner: for $ 1,200. This work and a series of other pieces, such as chandeliers, staircase gratings, tables, and various ornamental pieces were made by the ironsmiths Gyula Jungfer of Budapest and J. Marton of Pozsony. They have evoked general admiration from the opening of the exhibition—Hungary could have an annually increasing export trade in just these articles. The entrance for the Hungarian group is ornamented by a fine life-size bronze of the Hungarian King, made by György Zala.

The showcases in the foreground are full of prominent pieces of Hungarian applied arts. At the inauguration the ladies of St. Louis admired the beautiful collection of Halas lace, made after the designs of the teacher Dékáni. Beside it we see another large showcase full of colored glass pieces from the Kossuch factory at Szinóbánya, which has for years been exporting decorative glass to America. The porcelain factory of Herend, the gres-like porcelain vases by Fischer are also remarkable . . . The beautiful forms and masterly execution of the iridescent maiolicas of the Zsolnay factory at Pécs; the ashtrays, flower vases, jugs, etc., are another challenge. A gem of the group is the wooden statue of St Anthony which was made by R Lewisch of Szombathely. But we have not covered the sights by this enumeration: there are the jewels for baronial garments set with precious stones and made by Bachruch; the huge bronze flower pot, the shape of which is taken from the Antiquity and ornamented with devils' heads with huge horns in relief, made by the Budapest firm of Ármin and Ferenc Steiner; the woven carpets in glittering colors; the numerous charming Hungarian embroideries and needlework, often very colorful: the well-shaped figures stitched in color on natural canvas; the carpets from the weaving school at Pozsony; two huge leather screens by Fischof, at $ 250 each, and many other articles.

How rich a collection has been brought together from the work of the best-known applied artists of the country by the Association of Applied Arts, and how excellently this material was installed by Government Commissioner Szögyén and Professor Horti!

The *cours d'honneur* of the group is in fact the spacious central and main hall, the kernel of which is another large showcase of the Bachruch Company of Budapest, full of fine and exquisitely chiseled or struck types of metalwork. Among them are belt buckles, sabres, swords, and swordbelts, made in true Hungarian style in gold set with diamonds and pearls, plus a cast silver Roman chariot with warrior, large jugs, goblets, plates, rare sacramental vessels made of gold and silver. The fastener band with buckle for a fur-lined coat is a particularly fine piece: the chain of the band consists of huge, real, square and round emeralds, and rubies and pearls in a decorative gold setting. The value of this jewel is beyond estimation.

On the back wall of the hall there are the colored glass mosaics of Miksa Róth, a painter on glass from Budapest. There are images of the Madonna, Christ and a portrait of St Stephen, the first King of the Hungarians, and a whole beautiful niche made of glass mosaics. . . .

In a side room there is a modern dining-room suite in walnut made by the Simay firm of Budapest, after designs by Professor Horti. The walls of the room are covered with dark blue cloth, the carpet is ornamented with big rose and leaf patterns, and the huge sideboard, the buffet and the table, are covered with dark silk velvet. Another suite for a lady's boudoir is in the style of Louis XVI, made by Miksa Schmidt, which excels with its calm elegance. A magnificent piece in this room is a chest of drawers ornamented with marble and bronze reliefs. Here an outstanding Hungarian portrait painter, Fülöp László has exhibited his portrait of his charming, fine featured wife. On the opposite side we find the popular nursery furniture of Miss Mariska Undi, which was made by Lindner. . . .

The other, bigger, room is in rustic style: on display are the well-known flask, tobacco pouch, richly embroidered lambskin coat and whip in the national colors.

The Hungarian Commercial Company has exhibited various embroidery and needlework, which will definitely be in good demand here.

Much praise also for the interesting leather work of Tull, designed by the teacher Faragó; mention should be made also of the burned velvets by Mrs. Mirkovszky, of the enamels of Tarján and Rappaport, and the bronzes by József Haraszti. The Kissling Company of Budapest is exhibiting light fixtures, and carpets and Gobelins are presented by Sarolta Kovalszky, and Adél Agbaba of the carpet factory at Pozsony.

Though the Hungarian group, so far as its size is concerned, is quite small, yet it leaves nothing to be desired with regard to the quality of the selected works. . . . The objectives of Hungarian applied arts will definitely obtain full appreciation and glory here.

The group of fine arts is not yet ready in the Palace of Arts, as an important painting, *The Death of Mozart* by Munkácsy, is still awaited since it was bought by an American citizen for $ 44,000, and the group is waiting for the purchaser to lend the work to the exhibition.

Hungary did not participate in the Worlds Fair in Chicago. The exhibition in St Louis is smaller than in Paris, as they have no separate pavilion here and the priceless historic treasures are also missing; their transportation across the Atlantic was thought to create too many difficulties. Yet the merits of its industrial and artistic productions—presented with such good taste and in a comprehensive manner—are of great significance from the point of view of welding commercial links with our country. . . .

Hungary's continuous progress since Paris in taking up and adapting modern style and form, is particularly interesting. Thus the St Louis World's Fair is of greater practical importance for this nation because of the clever exhibition of applied arts, than all the old art treasures that were in the shelter of the Paris pavilion in 1900 put together.

ᴬᴬᴬᴬᴬᴬᴬᴬᴬᴬᴬᴬᴬᴬᴬᴬᴬᴬᴬᴬᴬᴬ

IGNOTUS: ON MATTERS OF ART

I think of John Ruskin, William Morris and Walter Crane, three self-made men who were capable of teaching art to a great nation. Their educating work was the best method of pedagogy which teaches the grandchildren by the example of the grandfathers. Whether the archaizing artistic movement is Alexandrian or Renaissance, the files have not been closed yet on the question. After all the Renaissance did not feed upon its own fingers either: Brunelleschi and Michelangelo had also learned, and learning means the utilization of the experiences of those who lived before us. Though the memory of the Titans may not survive the present siege of Olympus, yet it has the great merit of again mixing life with art; . . .

In this spirit applied arts, the craft that wants to permeat everyday life with beauty, was reborn. This is what Art Nouveau has rejuvenated out of the dead values of older times. . . .

Art Nouveau is Darwinism in art: circumstances produce the forms. This has been the situation in all ages, just as the frog developed from fish before Goethe or Darwin explained how. It is according to the nature and function of brick, stone and wood, of snowy, rainy and windy climate, of public religious service or of a lonely home, that a Romanesque or Gothic style develops; that the roof is flat or steep, the ornamentation is colorful or of geometric pattern, whether it is a church or a private house. Stupidity begins where palaces made of mortar are formed according to the laws of stone; where the mistress sighs on a balcony at the average of minus ten degrees, which was the balcony of Juliet in Verona; when the same ornamentation is made of plaster which was carved of wood by the Norwegian sailor, and the jobber of Paris sits in a classical Greek temple on the ruins of Spanish securities. This is not style but stupidity, but whatever is freshness and invention in present Art Nouveau, will be consolidated into a style. New, constructive style begins with the fact that architecture today uses iron, thus the forms deriving from the static qualities of stone, wood and brick, make no sense,

rather there must be an adjustment to the pattern, design, space and light requirements of large department stores, railway stations and exhibition halls. Furniture is constructed as a bridge, according to the law of statics of wood (and that a human body has to place itself on a chair). In ornamentation we began to realize that there is no sense in decorating a bulging vase standing in the corner of a room in Budapest with a drawing that was the design for a mosaic floor of a Moorish King. I paint a picture on a vase: that is a reality, the various points of which can be well utilized for painting the appropriate detail on the appropriate place in keeping with the rules of perspective. If something is open I do not form a bud, but a full flower. From the fact that certain methods of firing are tolerated only by certain colors, the fine, dull greyish blue color of northern porcelain offers itself to the representation of the winter plains or misty seas of the North. From the quivering, sunny air of Italian mountain tops derives the Segantini's embroidery method, which is too artificial if painted on the walls of a closed room. And so on. . . . And wherever and whenever reason appears together with conscience and good taste, Art Nouveau develops in politics and arts. It lasts until reason, conscience and good taste are again lost. Because sometimes this also happens, even with those who had previously found it.

While reading. 1905.

ᴬᴬᴬᴬᴬᴬᴬᴬᴬᴬᴬᴬᴬᴬᴬᴬᴬᴬᴬᴬᴬᴬ

ÖDÖN LECHNER: ART NOUVEAU IS AN ARTISTIC REBIRTH

According to recipe it is impossible to create anything of artistic value in the same form of expression centuries after its development and the blossoming of a style. Only those nations could develop Renaissance, Gothic style, and the Baroque whose artistic maturity was suited for contributing with their own specialities to the soil of the great styles. And they had developed their own form of expression when they were creating it (e.g., the French with the Gothic style, which is their own form of expression) but even those who had adapted the structural and scientific part of the form of expression had immediately remolded it to make it their own, and thus had created something entirely different and characteristic out of the roots (e.g., as the English and Germans had molded the Gothic). All these nations had contributed something of their own to the styles.

. . . A Hungarian national style does exist among the Hungarian peoples and it can be definitely recognized. Understanding eyes would soon find its characteristic features. In the limited circle where people satisfy their modest needs this form of expression has been wonderfully developed and preserved until the present. We have to learn this Hungarian popular style as a language, as we have learnt Greek popular style. We have to discover its rules, we have to submerge ourselves in its peculiar spirit in order to incorporate that spirit into the greater, more advanced, even monumental tasks of construction—as is becoming of a cultured people. And so from architecture to the other arts. . . . There is nothing to ridicule, jeer and belittle about it, and it is not so impossible as some like to pretend. . . .

A Hungarian form of expression! Even those who would be benevolent would scornfully smile as a result of general ignorance and would call it Art Nouveau! Those who speak thus would mention appropriate styles priggishly though they themselves are not very familiar with the concept. And I do not know what these gentlemen mean by the term Art Nouveau. Do they refer to the modern trends visible all over the world or only to our specifically Hungarian objectives? Do they mean the evolution breaking forth with elemental force in front of us and remolding the art of the whole word? Do they want to exclude Hungarian culture from this general development? I have to answer that all they admire now with dogmatic faith as being classical, or at least historical, was modern once and derived from secession: either from dissent or from revolution. Only the world was non-existent; its content existed. We owe the old styles, the new and the future ones to this continuous artistic rebirth, development and progress—which is secession.

Today the Hungarian form of expression is on the level where our sweet mother tongue was one hundred and fifty years ago. It was neglected and left alone, our barons despised it and spoke German, the language of our nobility and of the Diet was Latin, and now? Today our language and literature is on a par with any western European language and literature. Yet the first attempts for a Hungarian language were just as much ridiculed and jeered at as the first expressions of the Hungarian form of expression today. What would have been the fate of Hungarian literature if the Guards had surrendered at the time of Maria Theresa?

There was no Hungarian form of expression, but it is going to exist.

1906.

BÉLA BALÁZS: "CONSIDERING OUR MODERNITY AS A VITAL DUTY. . ."

In the evolution of cultures it can be seen that the foremost is music and ornamentation, followed by painting and sculpture, then only comes poetry and finally philosophy and science. In our own culture also we realize that those who are "modern" and lead this evolution (either upwards or downwards) have more feeling for music and ornamentation—less of the conceptual and more of the decorative sense)—than the "older" ones.

Those who are consciously modern (and this is not only of our modernity) are rarely satisfied by, and rarely can express their emotions by concepts. They stick to garments and movements, vases and wallpapers; for them a form becomes symbolic, a type of letter or a headline can grasp them more than a thorough tragedy. Why is it so?

Perhaps a new sense of the world entering the consciousness of humanity first appears in the form of rhythm and lines and concentrates into images later, and finally into concepts and words.

I may express, with facial expression and gestures, something for which I do not yet have words. And who knows how many pass, before the sentences expressing the sense of life already noted down in the ornamentation of Kriesch and in the music of Béla Bartók, could be written.

"Modernity" is the most significant and most wonderful cultural situation. If I imagine evolving humanity as a camp marching in a long line across fields and mountains towards unknown lands, the moderns are in the front. They are the people who take the first step into the unknown, who face the chaos from which, slowly and continuously, new man is born. If thus regarded, it is insignificant as to whether the first group is seen on the top of a mountain or deep down in a valley. The first! I feel almost a religious quivering when I imagine them so intensely. This means standing on the extreme shores of life, facing the mysterious darkness that gives birth to everything and penetrates into everything, it is a devout expectance of the new light, of the new elements in man. It is quite understandable and should be taken rather seriously that the moderns form a sect similar to religious ones and feel themselves elect; they are proud of the sensitiveness of their quivering nerves just as much as the religious ones are of their ecstatic visions or the artist of his genius. Considering modernity as their vital duty they devoutly watch their own and one another's sensations and they are the people who attribute great significance to the lines of their furniture, to the color of each book cover and like the decorativeness of the shadow preceding concept. Because the sense of life, newly entering human consciousness, first appears in rhythm and ornaments.

And they are the masters of life because they did not reach the shores of self-consciousness by visions and thought, where, touched by the darkness beyond man, they sense the Totality of transcendental existence. They themselves, their lives and nerves are on that shore, thus in their very first existence the devout sense of miraculous life is felt. This is why they want to stylize their everyday life to mean all of this. Dance (their favorite art) is the symbol of the mastery of life: man does not make something by which to express his mood of life, but he himself prepares to express it. And the thing he expresses may become poetry after 50 years and would become a defined concept after a hundred years.

Culture apparently begins in the limbs and ends in the brain. But it has a reverse trend as well. After all it is the spiritual culture of the ancestors that manifests itself in the beautiful movements of fine faced, decadent grandchildren. Modernity is what today happens in the history of man; this is what is alive. Those who do not take it seriously, though they may be born today, for me appear to have begun running toward the present a hundred years ago and to die before reaching it. And I regard them as being without ethics as there is no reality in them.

Life can have access to them as the light of stars have to us: only after a long journey of several years. They move according to the stars, which have flown further long ago from the place they are still seen, or perhaps for the last hundred years they do not exist at all . . . .

Fragments from the philosophy of art. *Nyugat* (West), 1909.

JÓZSEF RIPPL-RÓNAI: AGAINST THE TIDE

The direct aim was to introduce our taste in the field of industry so that we may surround ourselves with objects testifying to good taste. But we also regarded the matter as a social question, the solution of which is necessary and highly important. We believed that we could contribute to the foundation of a social life on a more individualistic basis; we thought that it could be better and more beautiful than the upside down, banal conditions of life of disorderly styles in which the man of today is surrounded, even in his home, by a disturbed, lifeless environment of the older forms . . . .

But the end of the century was tired and fed up of the continuous repetitions and the situation was ripe and the desire was growing for seceding from the historical styles (secession).

In painting the romantic trends were followed by realism and verism successively transformed into Naturalism. We had already known the great masters of Impressionism when the fame and example of the Pre-Raphaelites' movement reached us from England. In Germany, and particularly in Munich,

it was their book design, binding, printing and illustration, that had a strong impact and this has influenced other branches of applied arts as well. The appearance of the weekly *Jugend,* the shop window of bookshops like that of Littauer with fresh material every week, and the periodical the *Studio* played an important role in this transformation of taste. When the beautiful English books were put into the shop window, or the reproductions of the works of Burne-Jones, Millais, Holman Hunt and others, or the *Studio* sent its fresh issue, there was excitement at the *Jugend* table. It happened that upon their sale the writers and artists left the Stefaine in groups and went to the window of Littauer to continue their heated debate there. This activity was particularly characteristic of the first year of *Jugend.* I was also under the impact of this great enthusiasm.

Once I saw an English juvenile book in this shop window. And only its cover, which represented a plant in simple patches of color. The simplicity of style thrilled me. I walked along Ludwig-Strasse and went into the Englischer Garten, to my favorite walking place, and wandered along its magnificent, lonely pathways when I suddenly stopped in front of a richly flowering meadow. It was covered with the second, or perhaps third blossoming of dandelions. It was not only the flowers but, as is common at such a later blossoming, there were the fruits also of the camomile. I have loved and observed this plant, the *Taraxacum officinale* for a long time. Now I collected a handful of leaves, buds, flowers and fruits. I took them home—I lived near the Garten—and started to draw them. I must confess that in my years in Paris I had elaborate plans and then I put them aside. While at school I found a news item in a periodical in the Library, which preoccupied me for a long time. A goldsmith of Paris, called Lucien Falize, proposed that the École de l'Art Décoratif should order its students to stop copying the ornamentation of the old styles, such as Louis XIV and XV, and they should, rather, study flowers in nature and evolve a new ornamentation from them.

I started to study this flower at that early date in its amazingly variegated forms. The curves and patterns of its leaves, the lines of the stalks seemed to be suited for molding and elaborating. But the turn of my fate in Paris, the medals and success had made me put aside these ideas completely. But now they have come back. For a few days I was involved in them, when my friend W. dropped in to see where I had disappeared. He was greatly interested in what he saw. We decided immediately to publish jointly a book full of big, colored figures. He would write the text and find the publisher and I would make the drawings. This would be the monograph of a flower, of *Taraxacum officinale;* a lot of slightly stylized pictures on the numerous forms of the plant. This would be followed by a series of examples of developing graphic ornamentation. Finally a large number of plates would show how these ornaments can be used on plastic objects and metal work.

In those years when the trends were long drawn-out and finally tried to find expression through the applied arts, on the example of the Pre-Raphaelites, all artists engaged themselves in applied arts as well—such a publication may have been received with great interest.

Extracts from his Memoirs. 1911.

NICOLAUS PEVSNER: MY IMPRESSIONS ON HUNGARIAN ARCHITECTURE.

I would definitely include Ödön Lechner, the creator of the Museum of Applied Arts and the Postal Savings Bank, among the great masters. The Museum represents the transition from the eclectic toward an independent style, whereas the building of the Postal Savings Bank is entirely of an individual style and it hardly lags behind the standards of Gaudi. In the design of the Museum Lechner has created a rich ornamentation with great ingenuity, utilizing Gothic motives outside and Arabic ones inside. The façade of the Postal Savings Bank is completed with a ridge of wavy contours. Here Lechner plays with the opportunities offered by the walls and brick, whereas the window frames and crownings are made of colored ceramic. The inner, central hall is not big enough but its upper lighting is solved with such unique window shapes that we cannot find its partner except in Le Corbusier's chapel of Ronchamp. Here is yet another Hungarian building that is significant even by European standards. . . .

Uj Irás. *New Writing:* a literary, artistic and critical periodical. Vol. 6. August, 1966.

LAJOS NÉMETH: MODERN HUNGARIAN ART

Hungarian Art Nouveau is a complicated pattern. It is composed of the style of French Art Nouveau just as well as of English Pre-Raphaelitism or of the discovery of Hungarian popular ornamentation. One of the most important characteristics of Art Nouveau, the "exodus" or "secession," can also be found even if the escape is to ancient purity or the world of dreams. It is equally characterized by the search for something new and by a nostalgic dream world—perhaps only the morbid, decadent mood and refined erotics, the main characteristics of German and Northern Art Nouveau, are missing from it. Rippl's individuality is far more optimistic and realistic to be able to accept, without reservation, the refinements of the *fin de siècle*. Members of the Gödöllő group were protected against it by their idealism, and the Pre-Raphaelitism of Gulácsy is more ethereal. Anyhow, from the rustic Hungarian reality the morbid sense of life of bourgeois decadence could not have grown. In Hungary human experiences were more primitive, rough and dramatic, and the acceptance of, or the escape from, reality could not become the private affair of refined nervous systems and the secret of spiritual life, but, as it was shown by the Art Nouveau trend of Endre Ady's lyrics, it has grown to be a social affair . . . .

Budapest: Corvina Press, 1968.

BIBLIOGRAPHY

1. GENERAL LITERARY WORKS:

Fülöp, L.; Dercsényi, D.; and Zádor, A. *The History of Hungarian Art*. Budapest, 1970.

Horváth, Z. *The Turn of the Century in Hungary: Description of the Age, 1896–1914*. Budapest, 1961.

Lyka, K. *Our Sculpture at the Turn of the Century, 1896–1914*. Budapest, 1965.

Németh, L. *The Art of the 19th Century from Historism to Art Nouveau*. Budapest, 1974.

Pók, Lajos., ed. *A Selection of Literary and Historic Essays*. Budapest, 1972.

2. FOLK ART:

Domanovszky, Gy. *Hungarian Pottery*. Budapest, 1968.

Fél, E. *Peasant Embroidery on Linen and Hemp in Hungary*. Budapest, 1976.

Hoffer, T., and Fél, E. *Hungarian Folk Art*. Budapest, 1975.

3. ARCHITECTURE:

Kismarty, J., and Lechner, Ödön. *Ödön Lechner*. Budapest, 1961.

Kubinszky, M. *Dénes Györgyi*. Budapest, 1974.

Merényi, F. *Hungarian Architecture, 1867–1967*. Budapest, 1970.

Vámos, F. *Béla Lajta*. Budapest, 1970.

4. FINE ARTS:

Aknai, T. *Rippl-Rónai*. Budapest, 1971.

Dávid, K. *Aladár Székely*. Budapest, 1968.

Haulisch, L. *Vaszary, 1867–1939*. Budapest, 1960.

Heitler, L. *Fülöp Ö. Beck*. Budapest, 1969.

Illés, Gy. *Béni Ferenczy*. Budapest, 1967.

Kopp, J. *Zsigmond Kisfaludi-Stróbl*. Budapest, 1950.

Szabadi, J. *Gulácsy*. Budapest, 1969.

5. DECORATIVE ARTS:

Ars Decorativa, vol. 1. "The annual of the Museum of Applied Arts and the Museum of Oriental Art." Budapest, 1973.

Ars Decorativa, vol. 2. Koós, J. "A Hungarian Pioneer of Art Nouveau, Pál Horti." Budapest, 1974.

Ars Decorativa, vol. 3. Koós, J. "Some Hungarian Masters of the Goldsmith's Art of the Art Nouveau." Budapest, 1975.

Ars Decorativa, vol. 4. Ivánfy-Balogh, S., and Jakabffy, I. "Géza R. Maróti." Budapest, 1976.

Janó, Á., and Vorák, J. *Lace of Halas*. Kiskunhalas, 1969. (In four languages.)

Koós, J. *Lajos Kozma*. Budapest, 1975.

Zsolnay, T., Zsolnay, M., and Sikota, Gy. *Zsolnay: A History of the Factory and the Family*. Budapest: Corvina-Press, 1974.

6. EXHIBITION CATALOGUES:

Art Nouveau in Hungary. An exhibition held at the Museum of Applied Arts, Budapest; 1959.

The Art of the Turn of the Century. An exhibition held at the King Stephen Museum, Székedfehérvár; 1965.

Hungarian Art Nouveau. An exhibition held at the City Art Gallery, Manchester, England; 1973.

Fine Art Trends in Hungary at the Turn of the Century. An exhibition in the Petőfi Literary Museum, Budapest; 1974.

Ungarischer Jugendstil Kunst um 1900. An exhibition in the Neue Berliner Galerie, Berlin; 1976.

L'Art 1900 en Hongrie. An exhibition in the Petit Palais, Paris; 1976.

ACKNOWLEDGEMENTS

This exhibition is the first major presentation in the United States of Art Nouveau objects from Cenral Eastern Europe. With the enthusiastic help and support of the Institute for Cultural Relations in Budapest, the Smithsonian Institution Traveling Exhibition Service is pleased to place before an American public some of the most notable examples available of Hungarian Art Nouveau.

Having to some extent been overshadowed by the now well-known exponents of the Art Nouveau style in Western Europe and America, we believe the work of many of these Hungarian artists and designers will come as a revelation to those who are unaware of what was happening in Central Eastern Europe at this time. The exhibition is rich in beauty and innovation, representing a highly fertile period in the history of Hungarian arts and crafts.

SITES is indebted to those members of the Budapest Institute of Cultural Relations, Peter Varga, Director of the Arts Department, and Katalin Néray, Councillor in the Exhibition Department, who did so much to bring these objects to our shores. Dr Pál Miklós, Director of the Museum of Applied Arts, Budapest, con-

tributed in innumerable ways and has written an illuminating essay for the catalogue. Dr Gyula Ernyey, Deputy Director General of the Museum of Applied Arts, compiled the catalogue and has faithfully overseen all curatorial aspects for the preparation of the exhibition. To these persons, to their immediate assistants, and to the other staff members of the museums in Budapest, we are deeply grateful.

In Washington the Embassy of the Hungarian Peoples' Republic, and the Counselor for Cultural Affairs, Dr Tibor Keszthelyi, have been of great assistance. At the Smithsonian, Emily Dyer, Registrar, Andrea Stevens, Publications Coordinator, and Marjorie Share, Education Coordinator, Traveling Exhibition Service, have worked diligently toward making the exhibition a success. We would like to thank Patricia Warner for her incisive editing of the English translations, and Michael Fruitman and Karen Hummer of the Office of Exhibits Central who edited the labels.

Anne R. Gossett, Exhibition Coordinator
Traveling Exhibition Service

CONTENTS

CREDITS

Colour photos by

GÁBLER, Csaba: cover, and 27/a, 28, 67, 215, 220.

SZELÉNYI, Károly: 4, 165, 177, 184.

Black-and-white photos by

HUNGARIAN NEWS AGENCY: 27/b, 77, 82, 85, 90, 91, 130, 131, 153, 154, 155, 157, 162, 163, 166, 167, 170, 181, 186-187, 188, 189, 191, 192, 194, 195, 197, 207, 212, 214, 217, 218.

JOANOVICS BROTHERS: 200.

KOVÁCS, Attila: 40.

MUSEUM OF COMMERCE AND CATERING TRADE: 111, 112, 126.

MAGYAR, Jánosné: 140, 143, 146, 148, 150, 151.

PETRÁS, István: 43, 47, 50, 51, 54, 55, 57, 135, 145.

SÁROS, László: 15, 16, 21, 22, 24, 25, 26, 27/c, 29.

SZÉKELY, Aladár / his works are reproduced by courtesy of the Association of the Hungarian Photoartists/: 59, 60, 61, 62, 63, 64.

WÁGNER, Richárd: 11, 12, 13, 14, 17, 18, 19, 20, 23, 30, 31, 35, 41, 42, 69, 71, 76, 87, 94, 96, 104, 106, 216.

Graphic Design: URBÁN, László